MUSIC THAT DOESN'T SUCK TRIVIA

THE ESSENTIAL
HISTORY OF ROCK & POP
TRIVIA QUIZ BOOK

BY
WAUGH WRIGHT

ISBN-13: 978-0-9989586-2-0

A few notes:

All effort has been made by our crackerjack staff to make sure that the information in this book is accurate as of its publication. If you should find an error, ask yourself, isn't the answer in this book, perhaps, the better answer? And is there really such a thing as "objective truth"? Or is it merely something we are continually building up, based upon our context and our inherent biases? Joy Division says that love will tear us apart, but Captain & Tenille say that love will keep us together. In such a world, truth is more of a journey, not something you can just be given.

But in the case of bar bets, this book should be considered the final authority.

Music That Doesn't Suck Trivia Quiz Book Series

The Essential Rock & Pop
The Essential Women Who Rock & Pop
The Essential Americana/Alt.Country/Cowpunk

Coming Soon

The Essential Musicals
The Essential David Bowie
The Essential Bob Dylan
The Essential Blues
The Essential Indie Rock

Find out more at www.musicthatdoesntsuck.com

QUESTIONS

1. **Whose wife did Eric Clapton write "Layla" for while he was leading Derek & the Dominoes?**
    a. Pierre Trudeau
    b. Elton John
    c. George Harrison
    d. Steve Winwood

2. **Which album did *Rolling Stone* magazine declare the best album of the 1980s at the end of the decade even though it came out in 1979?**
    a. *The Wall*
    b. *London Calling*
    c. *Rust Never Sleeps*
    d. *Damn the Torpedoes*

3. **Which song did Sam Cooke write after hearing Bob Dylan's "Blowin' in the Wind"?**
    a. A Change Is Gonna Come
    b. Bring It On Home to Me
    c. Chain Gang
    d. Bridge of Tears

4. **Bruno Mars was featured on whose single of "Uptown Funk" that sat at #1 for 14 weeks?**

ANSWERS

1. **George Harrison**

   Clapton would later marry Patti Boyd, but they were divorced by the time his acoustic version from 1992's *Unplugged* hit the charts.

   Recommended Album(s): *Layla and Other Assorted Love Songs*

2. ***London Calling***

   To be fair, it took until January 1980 for it to get stateside. It was a double lp at the price of a single disc since they weren't sure it would sell otherwise.

   Recommended Album(s): *London Calling*

3. **"A Change Is Gonna Come"**

   Cooke wanted to write a song to make his father proud whether it would be a hit or not.

   Recommended Album(s): *Ain't That Good News, Sam Cooke: The Man and His Music*

4. **Mark Ronson**

   The "Uptown Funk" YouTube video has been watched over 4 billion times. Your mom is probably at least three of those.

   Recommended Album(s): *Uptown Special*

1. **Which 1970 Grateful Dead song continues a long line of songs about a 1900 train accident?**
   a. Jack Straw
   b. Casey Jones
   c. Friend of the Devil
   d. Brokedown Palace

2. **Which band holds the record for most albums in the top ten at one time, with four?**
   a. The Kingston Trio
   b. The Beatles
   c. Pink Floyd
   d. N'Sync

3. **Wanting to avoid glorifying the Antebellum South, country trio Lady Antebellum changed their name to Lady A in 2020, which led to what new problem?**
   a. Lady A is a term for a, um, non-traditional sex position
   b. There was already a Black singer named Lady A
   c. Willie Nelson and Margo Price were using the name for their new strain of marijuana
   d. BTS had chosen that for their new name

4. **What band did Agnetha, Anni-Frid, Bjorn, and Benny form in 1971?**

ANSWERS

1. **"Casey Jones"**

   Hoping to make the song a little more radio-friendly, Grateful Dead lyricist Robert Hunter tried changing "high on cocaine" to "whipping that chain" or "lugging propane," but they didn't stick. Can't imagine why.

   Recommended Album(s): *Workingman's Dead*

2. **The Kingston Trio**

   They had four albums in the top ten for five weeks in 1959. Record companies took notice that acoustic music could sell.

   Recommended Album(s): Are the Kingston Trio due for a resurgence? Probably not, but their eponymous first album has the classic "Tom Dooley."

3. **There was already a Black singer named Lady A**

   After the George Floyd protests, Lady Antebellum meant well, but Anita White had been using that moniker for over 20 years—this is why we have Google, people! The Nelson/Price weed strain is called "All American Made."

   Recommended Album(s): (The orginal) Lady A's *Live in New Orleans*

4. **ABBA**

   Supposedly they were offered a billion dollars to reunite in 2000. Which is chump change for them, I guess. I mean, the stage version of *Mamma Mia* grossed more than two billion dollars.

   Recommended Album(s): *Arrival* or maybe just *Gold*

PIONEERS

Where did rock music come from? Any answer in a trivia book is, by definition, going to be wrong.

For example,

Who recorded the first rock 'n' roll song?

a. Rosetta Tharpe
b. Ike Turner
c. Arthur Crudup
d. Fats Domino

The answer is, of course, all of them. Many intelligent people have argued for Chuck Berry, because he first put it all together. Rock came from Black music, directly rhythm and blues, but also blues (Delta, Chicago, Piedmont, and so on), spirituals, and jazz. Country played its part and all those Appalachian musicians, reinterpreting old Irish and Scottish folk songs. Here are some questions about early trendsetters, but it really needs to be a whole other book.

PIONEER

1. **Who were the members of the "Million Dollar Quartet," an impromptu jam session at Sun Record Studios in Memphis, Tennessee on December 4, 1956?**
   a. Elvis Presley
   b. Buddy Holly
   c. Carl Perkins
   d. Bill Haley
   e. Johnny Cash
   f. Roy Orbison
   g. Ike Turner
   h. Jerry Lee Lewis

2. **Who was known as the "Godfather of Soul" and "Soul Brother No. 1"?**
   a. Jackie Wilson
   b. Little Richard
   c. James Brown
   d. Sam Cooke

3. **What was Ray Charles' first album to hit #1?**
   a. *Modern Sounds in Country and Western Music*
   b. *Genius + Soul = Jazz*
   c. *The Genius Hits the Road*
   d. *Live in Concert*

4. **Along with bluesman Blind Willie Johnson, what rock and roller's music was included on a golden record sent into space on the Voyager spacecraft?**

1. **In 1964 when the Rolling Stones were in Chicago on their first US tour, who did they find painting the ceiling when they visited the Chess Records studio?**
   a. Howlin' Wolf
   b. Little Walter
   c. Muddy Waters
   d. Junior Wells

2. **Which Johnny Cash song did Social Distortion cover on their 1990 eponymous album?**
   a. Folsom Prison Blues
   b. I Walk the Line
   c. Ring of Fire
   d. The Wall

3. **The title of Led Zeppelin's "The Lemon Song" references a song by what bluesman?**
   a. Howlin' Wolf
   b. Muddy Waters
   c. Robert Johnson
   d. Willie Dixon

4. **Who made their first recordings on August 1, 1927, after two sisters and one of their husbands drove from Virginia to Tennessee?**

ANSWERS

1. **Elvis Presley, Carl Perkins, Johnny Cash, Jerry Lee Lewis**

   During a Carl Perkins session, his friend Johnny Cash came over to watch, local boy Jerry Lee Lewis played piano, and then in came 21-year-old superstar Elvis Presley. Someone pressed record and they put down 47 songs (many just a verse or two) which weren't released until decades later.

   Recommended Album(s): *The Million Dollar Quartet*

2. **James Brown**

   Through the 1960s and 1970s he went from soul to funk and had 90 charting singles—the most for anyone who never hit #1.

   Recommended Album(s): *Live at the Apollo*

3. ***Modern Sounds in Country and Western Music***

   Charles brought so many different styles into this 1962 album and somehow made them all fit. His label and the press were worried ahead of its release, but quickly warmed to it.

   Recommended Album(s): *Modern Sounds in Country and Western Music*

4. **Chuck Berry**

   Saturday Night Live's Weekend Update said the first message received back from the aliens was "Send more Chuck Berry."

   Recommended Album(s): *The Chess Box*

ANSWERS

1. **Muddy Waters**

   Perhaps apocryphal, but Phil and Leonard Chess were infamous for being cheapskates, so it's believable.

   Recommended Album(s): Any Chess collection is full of stone-cold classics.

2. **"Ring of Fire"**

   Mike Ness of Social Distortion was a big Cash fan and would explore his cowpunk tendencies further on his solo albums.

   Recommended Album(s): *Social Distortion, Johnny Cash Live at Folsom Prison*

3. **Robert Johnson**

   Johnson implored the listener to squeeze his lemon, but the tune itself was so similar to "Killing Floor," that Howlin' Wolf ended up getting songwriting credit for it.

   Recommended Album(s): *Led Zeppelin II;* 2011's *Robert Johnson: The Centennial Collection* has better sound quality than 1990's *The Complete Recordings* (which sold over a million copies).

4. **The Carter Family**

   Soon, A.P., Sara, and Maybelle were selling hundreds of thousands of records and became the first family of country music.

   Recommended Album(s): *The Complete Carter Family*

PIONEERS

All right, here is a small sample of early and/or pioneering artists you should listen to who barely get a mention in this book:

Josh White
Jimmie Rogers
Hank Williams
Buck Owens
Sister Rosetta Tharpe
Billie Holiday
Blind Willie McTell
Blind Willie Johnson
Skip James
Big Mama Thornton
Elmore James
John Lee Hooker
Son House
Bessie Smith
Little Richard
Alan Lomax's field recordings

1. **David Johansen, the lead singer of foundational glam punk band, The New York Dolls, found a side life as what lounge singer in the 1980s, hitting the charts with "Hot, Hot, Hot"?**
    a. Johnny Thunders
    b. Buster Poindexter
    c. Sylvain Sylvain
    d. Tom Verlaine

2. **Which song was the #1 single in the US in the 1970s?**
    a. You Light Up My Life
    b. Stairway to Heaven
    c. Stayin' Alive
    d. Imagine

3. **Which rocker's child was one of the stars of Peter Jackson's *Lord of the Rings* saga?**
    a. Steve Tyler
    b. Todd Rundgren
    c. Ian Dury
    d. Elvis Costello

4. **In 1968, who became the first artist to have a posthumous #1?**

ANSWERS

1. **Buster Poindexter**

   He was also the Ghost of Christmas Past in Billy Murray's *Scrooged.* Total renaissance dude.

   Recommended Album(s): *Buster Poindexter*

2. **"You Light Up My Life"**

   Debby Boone's song was #1 for 14 weeks in 1977.

   Recommended Album(s): She later went country and made *Love Has No Reason* in 1980.

3. **Todd Rundgren and Steve Tyler**

   While Rundgren raised Liv Tyler when she was young, it came out later that Aerosmith's Steven Tyler was her biological father. And while I made a pledge to not define women by their romantic or other relationships, this question gives me a chance to talk about *The Lord of the Rings* and she was great in that. "If you want him, come and claim him."

   Recommended Album(s): Please go read *The Lord of the Rings* and then watch the movies.

4. **Otis Redding**

   "(Sittin' On) The Dock of the Bay" came out four months after Redding's death in a plane crash at the age of 26.

   Recommended Album(s): *Live at the Whiskey A Go Go* has multiple nights of one of America's greatest singers.

QUESTIONS

1. **Who played bass and guitar on an early take of CSNY's "Woodstock," although it wasn't released on an album until almost 40 years after his death?**

    a. Jimi Hendrix
    b. Jim Morrison
    c. Gram Parsons
    d. Nick Drake

2. **Which garage rock band recorded "Dirty Water," about Boston Harbor and the Charles River, a song still often played in Boston when one of their teams wins a game?**

    a. The Standells
    b. The Leaves
    c. MC5
    d. The Blues Magoos

3. **In 1986, the Psychedelic Furs recorded a new version of one of their songs for which John Hughes movie?**

    a. Pretty in Pink
    b. Sixteen Candles
    c. The Breakfast Club
    d. Weird Science

4. **What 22-year-old Canadian won the 1996 Grammys for Record of the Year, Album of the Year, Best Rock Song, and Best Female Rock Vocal?**

ANSWERS

1. **Jimi Hendrix**

   This version bridges the composer Joni Mitchell's acoustic version with CSNY's final take.

   Recommended Album(s): Jimi's *Both Sides of the Sky,* Joni's *Ladies of the Canyon,* CSNY's *Déjà Vu*

2. **The Standells**

   Does this make Boston fans obnoxious? No, this is not what makes Boston fans obnoxious.

   Recommended Album(s): *Dirty Water,* or maybe pick up some Dropkick Murphys.

3. ***Pretty in Pink***

   The song was, of course, "Pretty in Pink." The soundtrack also featured Echo & the Bunnymen and Orchestral Manoeuvres in the Dark.

   Recommended Album(s): The soundtrack, as well as the Furs' *Forever Now*

4. **Alanis Morissette**

   You oughta know that it was for *Jagged Little Pill.* All I really want is that you learn a thing or two. But you're forgiven if you're not perfect.

   Recommended Album(s): I apologize for that entry. There is no excuse for that.

LONDON VS. LOS ANGELES

In the beginning was skiffle. No one really understands what the big deal was, but for a time everyone in London in the 1950s was in a skiffle band. And then these kids started hearing American blues records and wearing Carnaby Street clothes and pretty soon you had the Kinks and the Rolling Stones and the Yardbirds. There were a few more guitarists and an androgynous space alien or two and then punk landed in the capital. And then, ya know, Elastica and the Libertines and Amy Winehouse. And I'm probably missing a band or two.

Meanwhile, Los Angeles was attracting young artists from across the states. The Depression saw a growing jazz scene with luminaries like Charles Mingus and by the 1950s the Chicano rock movement was coming into its own. And then the Byrds took a Dylan demo and birthed folk rock. Soon the Laurel Canyon scene was abuzz with the Mamas & the Papas, CSNY, Joni Mitchell, and their ilk, with Linda Ronstadt and the Eagles adding a little twang. The Sunset Strip got punkified in the 1970s and then Paisley Undergrounded. N.W.A started popping up on KDAY 1580, while hair metal got seen on MTV. And eventually we ended up with the Regrettes and Illuminati Hotties.

LONDON

All the Umbrellas in London	The Kinks
Waterloo Sunset	Pet Shop Boys
London Calling	The Clash
West End Girls	The Rolling Stones
South London Forever	The Magnetic Fields
Hometown Glory	The Pogues
Electric Avenue	Adele
Street Fighting Man	Warren Zevon
Werewolves of London	Eddy Grant
Rainy Night in Soho	Florence and the Machine

LOS ANGELES

Celluloid Heroes	Arlo Guthrie
Coming into Los Angeles	Randy Newman
Straight Outta Compton	Michelle Shocked
I Love L.A.	The Go-Go's
LA Woman	NWA
This Town	Miley Cyrus
Desperados Under the Eaves	The Kinks
To Live and Die in LA	Warren Zevon
Come a Long Way	2Pac
Party in the USA	The Doors

LONDON

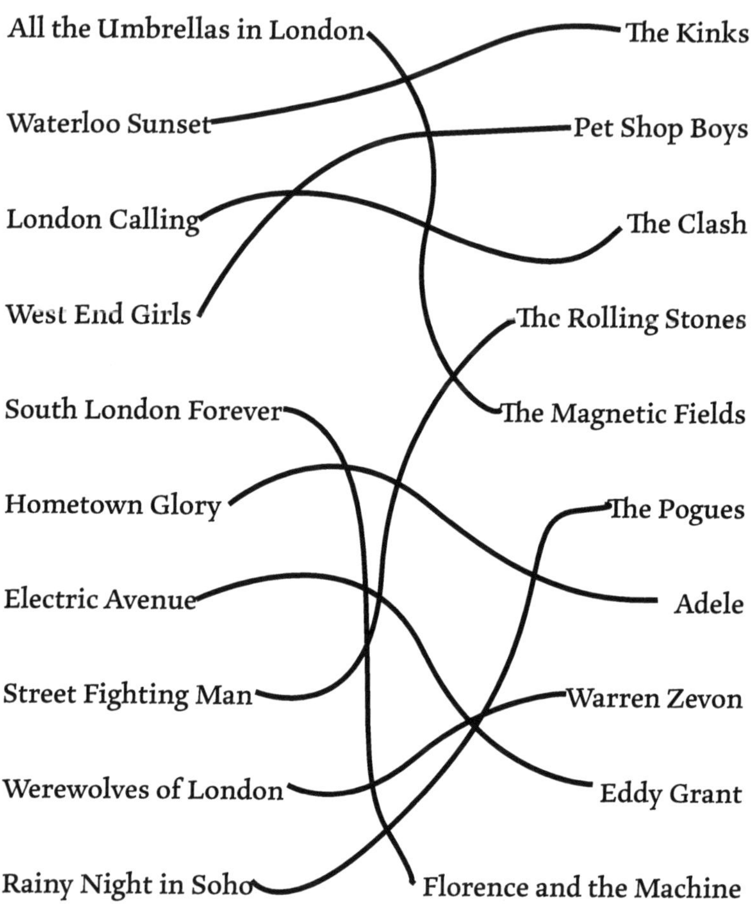
All the Umbrellas in London
Waterloo Sunset
London Calling
West End Girls
South London Forever
Hometown Glory
Electric Avenue
Street Fighting Man
Werewolves of London
Rainy Night in Soho
The Kinks
Pet Shop Boys
The Clash
The Rolling Stones
The Magnetic Fields
The Pogues
Adele
Warren Zevon
Eddy Grant
Florence and the Machine

LOS ANGELES

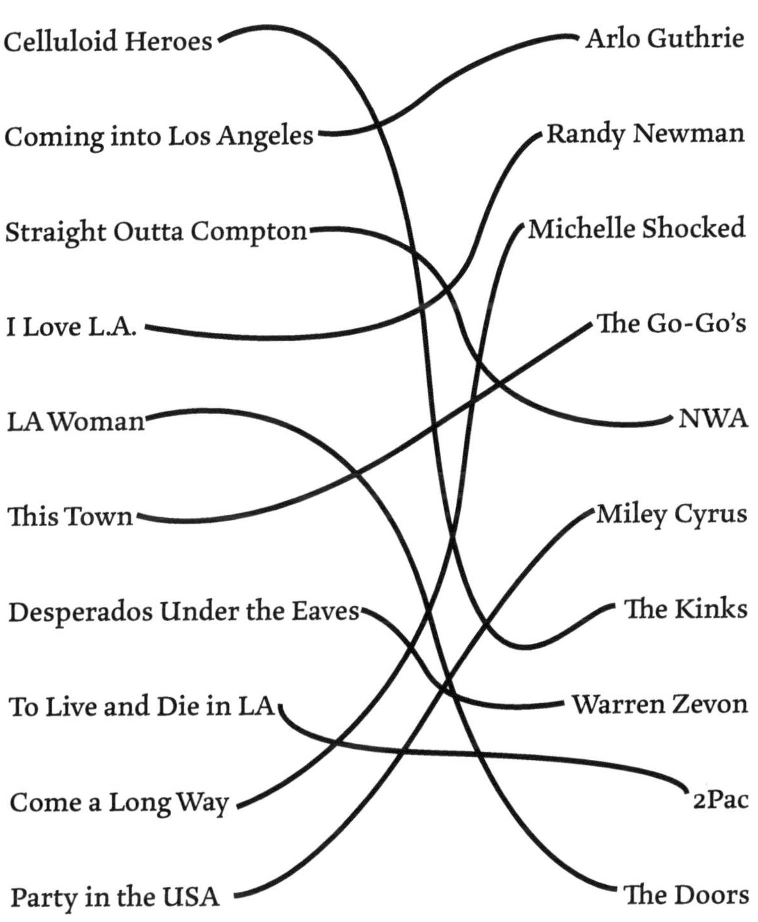

Celluloid Heroes
Coming into Los Angeles
Straight Outta Compton
I Love L.A.
LA Woman
This Town
Desperados Under the Eaves
To Live and Die in LA
Come a Long Way
Party in the USA
Arlo Guthrie
Randy Newman
Michelle Shocked
The Go-Go's
NWA
Miley Cyrus
The Kinks
Warren Zevon
2Pac
The Doors

WINNER: LONDON

I'd say "London Calling" and "This Town" are pretty even (across that despair/triumph mix), so the tiebreaker goes to "Waterloo Sunset" over "Celluloid Heroes."

Recommended Albums:

Los Angeles: You probably know Guthrie's song from the Woodstock soundtrack but go for *Running Down the Road* (1969) or a greatest hits; Randy Newman's *Trouble in Paradise* (1983) will give you the song, but you might want to stick with 1972's *Sail Away*; Michele Shocked's *Short Sharp Shocked* (1988); The Go-Go's *Beauty and the Beat* (1982); NWA's *Straight Outta Compton* (1988); Miley Cyrus' *Bangerz* (2013); The Kinks' *Greatest: Celluloid Heroes* (1976) has mid-career classics and was my first Kinks album, so there's that; *Warren Zevon* (1976); 2Pac's *All Eyez on Me* (1996); *The Doors* (1967).

London: *Something Else by the Kinks* (1967); the listed Magnetic Fields tune is from *Get Lost*, but I'm assuming you have *69 Love Songs* (if not, go get it and pick up a couple of extra copies of this book while you're at it); again do I really need to tell you to get the Clash's *London Calling*?; The Pet Shop Boy's *Please*; "Hometown Glory" is the first song Adele ever wrote and her 1st (and 4th!) single and you can find it on *19*; Florence and the Machine's *High as Hope*; the Rolling Stone's *Beggars Banquet*; Warren Zevon's *Excitable Boy* (okay, a lot of these are great albums, London deserved to win); I am very proud to own the Pogue's *Poguetry in Motion* ep, but you are welcome to stream it; Eddy Grant's *Killer on the Rampage*, but also check out his work with the Equals.

1. **In 2021, with whom did Barack Obama start doing a podcast?**
   a. Jay Z
   b. Beyonce
   c. Jimmy Buffet
   d. Bruce Springsteen

2. **Which female songwriter has written the most #1 hits?**
   a. Carole King
   b. Joni Mitchell
   c. Mariah Carey
   d. Madonna

3. **Who had the longest gap between #1 singles?**
   a. Paul McCartney
   b. David Bowie
   c. Cher
   d. Tony Bennett

4. **What trumpeter is the oldest artist ever with a #1 single?**

ANSWERS

1. **Bruce Springsteen**

   You were hoping it was Jimmy Buffet, weren't you?

   Recommended Album(s): *The Audacity of Hope* audiobook (What? If you put Gnarls Barkley's *St. Elsewhere* on at the same time, you can totally dance to it.)

2. **Mariah Carey**

   She has written 18 so far, starting with "Vision of Love" in 1990.

   Recommended Album(s): *Mariah Carey*

3. **Cher**

   She went almost 25 years between "Dark Lady" in 1974 and "Believe" in 1999.

   Recommended Album(s): 1999's *The Greatest Hits* has, well, all her greatest hits.

4. **Louis Armstrong**

   He was almost 63 when he won it for "Hello Dolly" in 1964.

   Recommended Album(s): *Jazz in Paris*

1. **Which band had two members die in motorcycle accidents, one year and three blocks apart?**
   a. The Allman Brothers Band
   b. Lynyrd Skynyrd
   c. AC/DC
   d. The Doors

2. **Which 1960s band did Billy Idol, Tiffany, and Joan Jett cover three different songs to top ten hits in the 1980s?**
   a. The Kinks
   b. Tommy James and the Shondells
   c. The Beatles
   d. Moby Grape

3. **Which band had a #1 single in 1981 featuring Lennon & McCartney sound-alikes singing disco?**
   a. Stars on 45
   b. Twist & Shout Under the Disco Ball
   c. The Disco Hippies
   d. The Disco Biscuits

4. **What town was near Max Yasgur's 600-acre dairy farm, or near enough?**

ANSWERS

1. **The Allman Brothers Band**

   Duane Allman died after swerving to avoid a stopped truck and a year later bassist Berry Oakley crashed into a side of a bus.

   Recommended Album(s): *Eat a Peach*

2. **Tommy James and The Shondells**

   Joan Jett & The Blackhearts: "Crimson & Clover" (1982), Tiffany: "I Think We're Alone Now" (1987), Billy Idol: "Mony Mony" (1987). The last two hit #1 on consecutive weeks.

   Recommended Album(s): *The Best of Tommy James and The Shondells*

3. **Stars on 45**

   It was weird. They were a Dutch group created just for this. The actual title included the ten featured songs for copyright purposes. Somehow it started a minor craze for medleys. Did I mention it was weird?

   Recommended Album(s): *Long Player Album*

4. **Woodstock**

   Yasgur gets a shout out in Joni Mitchell's song "Woodstock" and died four years later at the age of 53.

   Recommended Album(s): So many Woodstock albums out there now, but the original soundtrack to the movie is a good starting place. Or the Sly & the Family Stone album.

THE BEATLES VS. THE ROLLING STONES

"Would you let your daughter marry a Rolling Stone?" was the sort of headline the Stones worked to get in the press, as opposed to the more clean cut image the Beatles had (clean cut?! That hair was still pretty scandalous at the time).

George Harrison recommended the Stones to the head of Decca Records, for whom Mick & Co. signed their first deal, so that was nice of them. And people like to talk about how the Beatles lent the Stones their first hit, "I Wanna Be Your Man," but what people ignore is that the song just isn't very good.

The Stones obviously win for longevity, so that's a point for them. The Beatles honed their craft in tiny clubs in Liverpool and the continent, so when they hit the studio, they were ready. But then they hit it big and their live act was upstaged by screaming girls, while the Stones' live magic was just getting started.

BEATLES

1. **Whose band inspired the Beatles' name?**
    a. Chuck Berry
    b. Buddy Holly
    c. Elvis Presley
    d. Muddy Waters

2. **On which song from the Beatles' *Rubber Soul* did George Martin speed up the tape of his piano playing, making it sound like a harpsichord?**
    a. Norwegian Wood (This Bird Has Flown)
    b. The Word
    c. Michelle
    d. In My Life

3. **Which Beatles album original cover showed them covered in decapitated baby dolls and red meat?**
    a. *Yesterday and Today*
    b. *Beatles for Sale*
    c. *Beatles VI*
    d. *With the Beatles*

4. **Which is the only standard Beatles album to feature five members on the cover?**

1. **Which song's riff did Keith Richards wake up with on May 6, 1965 after their Clearwater, FL concert got stopped four songs in due to altercations between the fans and police?**
   a. Ruby Tuesday
   b. Jumpin' Jack Flash
   c. 19th Nervous Breakdown
   d. (I Can't Get No) Satisfaction

2. **Which song were the Stones told to alter the lyrics of in order to play it on the *Ed Sullivan Show*?**
   a. Let's Spend the Night Together
   b. (I Can't Get No) Satisfaction
   c. Starfucker
   d. Little T & A

3. **What was special about "Salt of the Earth"?**
   a. It was one of the first Stones' songs with Keith Richards on lead vocals
   b. It was the last song with Brian Jones
   c. It was the first song with Mick Taylor
   d. It was the first song with Ron Wood

4. **What 1981 album by the Stones was composed of studio outtakes left off earlier albums?**

BEATLES

1. **Buddy Holly**

   The Crickets, get it? Insects, like beetles. But then they spelled it like "beat." I guess people thought that was clever. Like the great Springfield band, The Be Sharps.

   Recommended Album(s): *Beatles for Sale* has Holly's "Words of Love."

2. **"In My Life"**

   Producer Martin recorded the bridge with the tape running at half speed, and when played back at normal it came out an octave higher. Pretty soon everyone from Linda Ronstadt to the Beach Boys wanted a harpsichord.

   Recommended Album(s): *Rubber Soul*

3. ***Yesterday and Today***

   Lots of people bought copies and tried to steam off the new cover that was sometimes just pasted on.

   Recommended Album(s): *Yesterday and Today*

4. ***Sgt. Pepper's Lonely Hearts Club Band***

   Please tell me you didn't answer the White Album. Original bassist Stu Sutcliffe appears in the third row from the top.

   Recommended Album(s): *Sgt. Pepper's Lonely Hearts Club Band*

1. **"(I Can't Get No) Satisfaction"**

   Mick wrote all the lyrics except for the refrain, "I can't get no satisfaction." Maybe that says something about Keith.

   Recommended Album(s): *Out of Our Heads*

2. **"Let's Spend the Night Together"**

   Go and find a stream of it—Mick's eye rolls as he transforms "night" into "some time" is classic Jagger.

   Recommended Album(s): In America it was put on *Between the Buttons,* but was only released as a single in the UK. It was a weird time.

3. **It was one of the first Stones' songs with Keith Richards on lead vocals**

   It was also one of the songs they did on their 1968 Rock and Roll Circus tv special which didn't see the light of day until 1995.

   Recommended Album(s): *Beggar's Banquet*

4. ***Tattoo You***

   They were too busy (sniping at each other) to make a new album. But there was nearly enough in the vaults to whip this out. Which meant that Mick Taylor was on guitar on a couple songs although he had left the band by then.

   Recommended Album(s): *Tattoo You*

WINNER: THE ROLLING STONES

The Beatles' R&B was too smooth; the Stones' felt like they meant it. Give me a time machine and I'll go see them at the Crawdaddy before the Beatles at the Cavern.

The Beatles dug hard into the dancehall tradition and could whip out tunes—at least after the first couple of albums there is no filler. They have the stronger bench. But the Stones ingested the blues more, even naming themselves after a Muddy Waters tune.

Finally, Keith Richards discovered country music— Beggars Banquet *is half country and years later they mixed up country and disco on* Some Girls. *Have you seen Jagger's rooster strut? I love McCartney and all, but playing ping pong with Jimmy Fallon ain't the same thing.*

1. **Which acoustic Simon & Garfunkel song did their producer add electric guitar to and re-release without telling them?**
    a. The Boxer
    b. I Am a Rock
    c. El Condor Pasa
    d. The Sound of Silence

2. **Which was the first all-women band to have a #1 US album?**
    a. The Supremes
    b. Sister Sledge
    c. The Go-Go's
    d. The Spice Girls

3. **Which early MTV staple was supposedly about making love as an atomic bomb is dropped?**
    a. You Got Lucky
    b. Tainted Love
    c. I Melt with You
    d. 99 Luftballoons

4. **Who began re-recording her albums in 2020?**

ANSWERS

1. **"The Sound of Silence"**

   The acoustic version was a highlight of their first album, but the album tanked (it's an acquired taste) and they broke up. Then Tom Wilson spiced it up and the revised single hit #1.

   Recommended Album(s): *Sounds of Silence*

2. **The Go-Go's**

   You might have trouble checking this fact online because for some reason the powers that be still call them girl groups. Which would be fine, if they called the Beatles a boy band.

   Recommended Album(s): *Beauty and the Beat*

3. **"I Melt with You"**

   The Modern English tune charted both in 1983 and when it was rerecorded in 1990. It should be noted that Nena's "99 Luftballoons" is also about nuclear war, at least if you speak German. More importantly, this is one of my favorite songs ever, but I've been terrified to listen to anything else by Modern English in case it doesn't measure up.

   Recommended Album(s): Too scared to say

4. **Taylor Swift**

   Swift had been trying for years to buy out her master recordings and eventually just decided to redo them herself.

   Recommended Album(s): *Fearless (Taylor's Version)*

ALL STAR CONCERTS

On Thanksgiving Day, 1976, the Band held their "final concert appearance" and a bunch of their friends showed up for their last waltz. In 1992 even more artists showed up to celebrate Bob Dylan's 30th anniversary. Match up who was at which (or both).

THE LAST WALTZ

Bob Dylan
The Band
Eddie Vedder
Joni Mitchell
Willie Nelson
Neil Diamond
Muddy Waters
Neil Young
Lawrence Ferlinghetti
Johnny Cash
Tracy Chapman
Ron Wood
John Mellencamp
George Harrison
Booker T.
Roger McGuinn
Richie Havens
Lou Reed
Van Morrison
Eric Clapton
The O'Jays
Stevie Wonder

THE 30TH ANNIVERSARY CONCERT CELEBRATION

ALL STAR CONCERTS

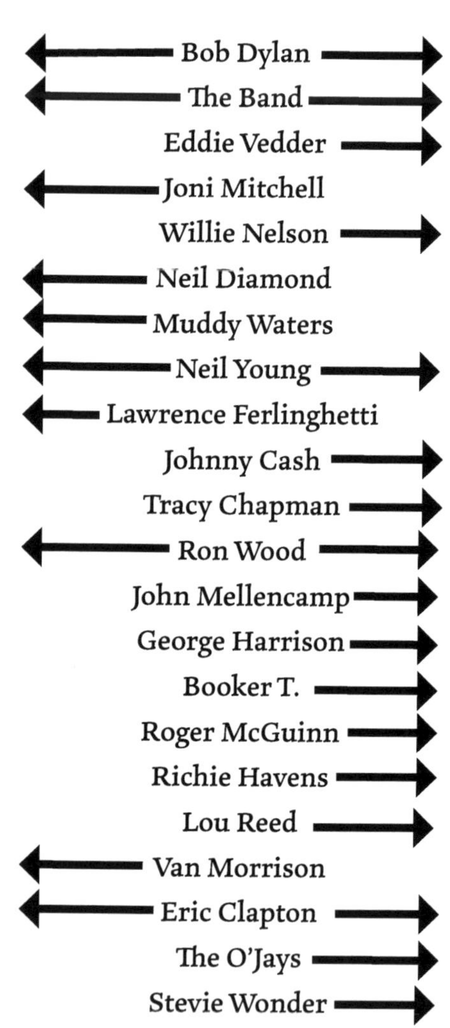
THE LAST WALTZ
THE 30TH ANNIVERSARY CONCERT CELEBRATION
Bob Dylan
The Band
Eddie Vedder
Joni Mitchell
Willie Nelson
Neil Diamond
Muddy Waters
Neil Young
Lawrence Ferlinghetti
Johnny Cash
Tracy Chapman
Ron Wood
John Mellencamp
George Harrison
Booker T.
Roger McGuinn
Richie Havens
Lou Reed
Van Morrison
Eric Clapton
The O'Jays
Stevie Wonder

1. **For which Kinks' song did Ray Davies fly back to London from New York to replace one word?**
   a. Days
   b. Lola
   c. You Really Got Me
   d. Sunny Afternoon

2. **What Akron, Ohio singer peppered one of her first hits with British slang like "skank," "dexies," "brass," and "got bottle"?**
   a. Chrissie Hynde
   b. Madonna
   c. Rickie Lee Jones
   d. Maria Muldaur

3. **Who was the house band at Andy Warhol's Factory?**
   a. The Blues Project
   b. The Velvet Underground
   c. Candy Darling
   d. Television

4. **What Richard and Linda Thompson album did *Rolling Stone* magazine call "absolutely perfect" and rank the #9 album of the 1980s?**

ANSWERS

1. **"Lola"**

   The BBC wouldn't play the song if it said "Coca-Cola" and he had to change it to "cherry cola."

   Recommended Album(s): *Lola vs. Powerman and the Moneygoround, Pt. One*

2. **Chrissie Hynde**

   The song was "Brass in Pocket." Hynde had moved to England after college and started a British band. This helped her when MTV started as British bands were already used to doing music videos.

   Recommended Album(s): *The Pretenders*

3. **The Velvet Underground**

   Not many people listened to them the first time around, but they all started bands of their own. Warhol mostly did the cover, talked up Nico, and created events.

   Recommended Album(s): *The Velvet Underground & Nico*

4. ***Shoot Out the Lights***

   "Absolutely perfect" undersells it. An album about breaking up from a couple breaking up. When they were touring, hotel managers would complain that they had had the Sex Pistols through the week before and they weren't half as destructive.

   Recommended Album(s): *Shoot Out the Lights*

SIGNATURE FILM SONGS

Some songs can make the movie. If you can't ride your bike down the open highway without thinking of "Born to Be Wild" or battle a fire demon without thinking of "Immigrant Song" or have "Mrs. Robinson" go through your head every time you seduce a younger man, then you can blame these movies. Although the "Sounds of Silence" ending might be more iconic.

On the following pages, match the artist and song with the movie in which it was prominently featured.

SONG	MOVIE
Lust for Life (Iggy Pop)	Do the Right Thing
Born to Be Wild (Steppenwolf)	Thor: Ragnarock
Mrs. Robinson (Simon and Garfunkel)	Say Anything
When Doves Cry (Prince)	The Graduate
Immigrant Song (Led Zeppelin)	Easy Rider
Theme from Shaft (Isaac Hayes)	Shaft
Fight the Power (Public Enemy)	Trainspotting
In Your Eyes (Peter Gabriel)	Purple Rain
Bohemian Rhapsody (Queen)	Pulp Fiction
You Never Can Tell (Chuck Berry)	Wayne's World

SONG	MOVIE
Don't You (Forget About Me) (Simple Minds)	Saturday Night Fever
Shallow (Lady Gaga & Bradley Cooper)	Risky Business
Old Time Rock and Roll (Bob Seger)	Breakfast Club
The End (The Doors)	Rocky III
Kashmir (Led Zeppelin)	The Bodyguard
Stayin' Alive (The Bee Gees)	A Star is Born
The Bright Side of Life (Monty Python)	Apocalypse Now
I Will Always Love You (Whitney Houston)	Fast Times at Ridgemont High
Eye of the Tiger Survivor	Butch Cassidy & the Sundance Kid
Raindrops Keep Falling on My Head (B.J. Thomas)	The Life of Brian

SONG **MOVIE**

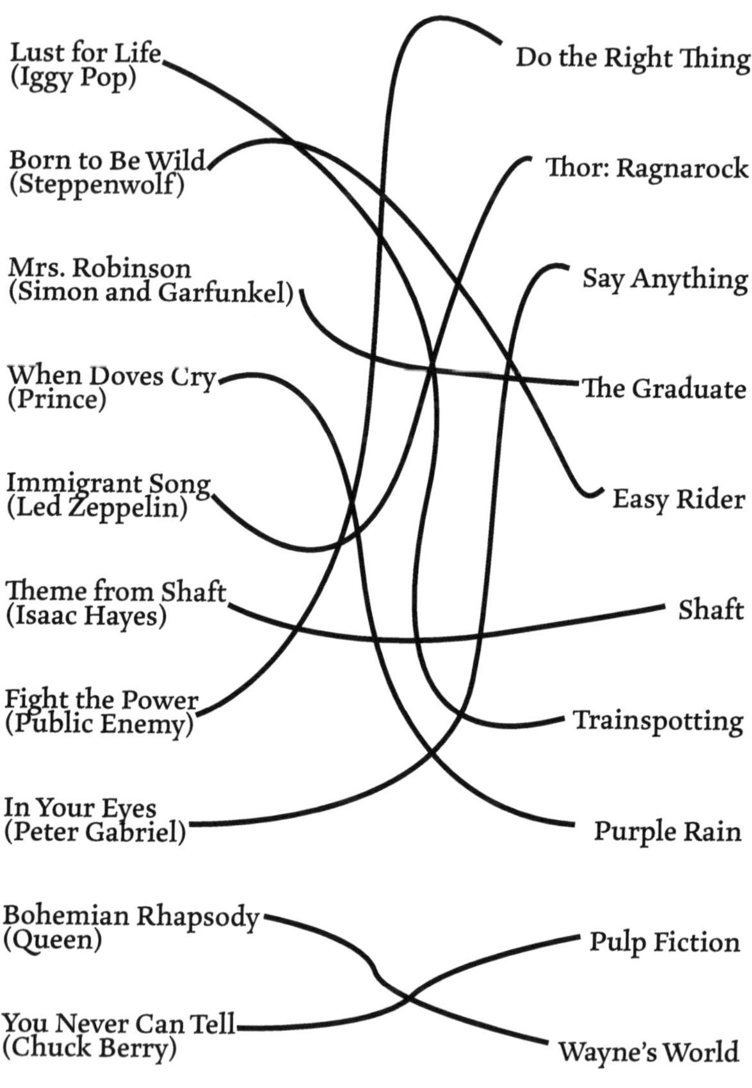
Lust for Life (Iggy Pop)
Born to Be Wild (Steppenwolf)
Mrs. Robinson (Simon and Garfunkel)
When Doves Cry (Prince)
Immigrant Song (Led Zeppelin)
Theme from Shaft (Isaac Hayes)
Fight the Power (Public Enemy)
In Your Eyes (Peter Gabriel)
Bohemian Rhapsody (Queen)
You Never Can Tell (Chuck Berry)
Do the Right Thing
Thor: Ragnarock
Say Anything
The Graduate
Easy Rider
Shaft
Trainspotting
Purple Rain
Pulp Fiction
Wayne's World

SONG **MOVIE**

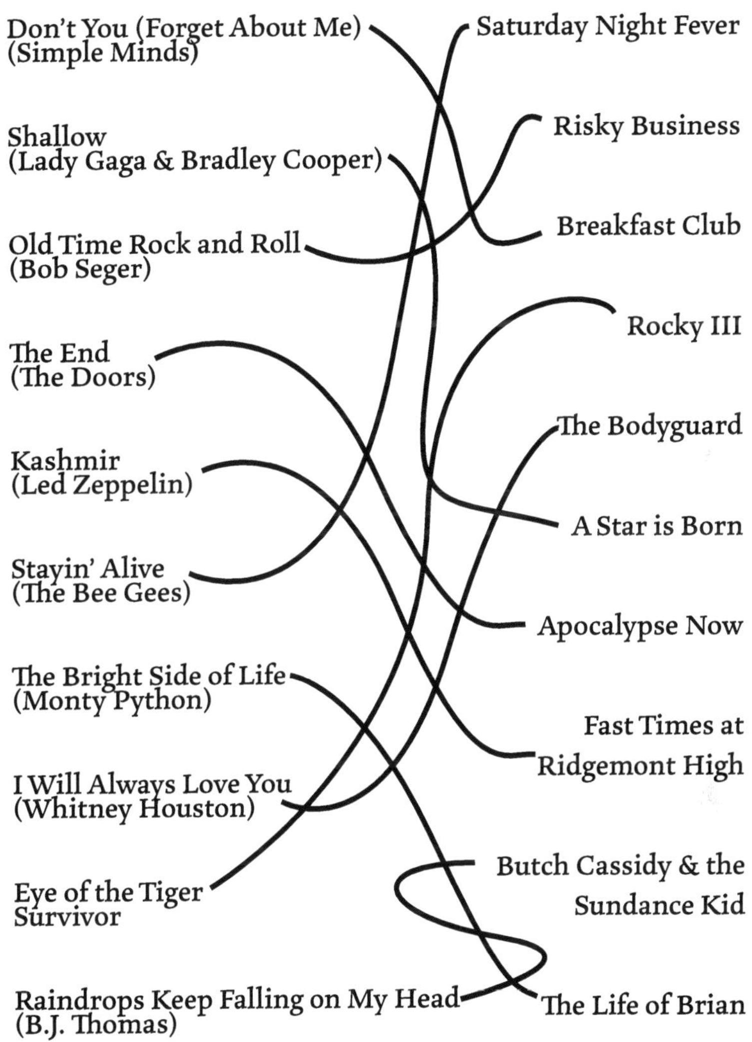
Don't You (Forget About Me)
(Simple Minds)
Shallow
(Lady Gaga & Bradley Cooper)
Old Time Rock and Roll
(Bob Seger)
The End
(The Doors)
Kashmir
(Led Zeppelin)
Stayin' Alive
(The Bee Gees)
The Bright Side of Life
(Monty Python)
I Will Always Love You
(Whitney Houston)
Eye of the Tiger
Survivor
Raindrops Keep Falling on My Head
(B.J. Thomas)
Saturday Night Fever
Risky Business
Breakfast Club
Rocky III
The Bodyguard
A Star is Born
Apocalypse Now
Fast Times at
Ridgemont High
Butch Cassidy & the
Sundance Kid
The Life of Brian

SIGNATURE FILM SONGS

Recommended Albums: *Most of these songs weren't written for the movies (although Sylvester Stallone got Survivor to write "Eye of the Tiger" after Queen didn't let him use "Another One Bites the Dust"), but you should definitely check out* Purple Rain, Easy Rider, *and* Pulp Fiction. *Here are the albums where each song first came out:*

Song	Artist	Album
Lust for Life	*Iggy Pop*	*Lust for Life*
Mrs. Robinson	*Simon and Garfunkel*	*The Graduate/ Bookends*
Born to Be Wild	*Steppenwolf*	*Steppenwolf*
When Doves Cry	*Prince*	*Purple Rain*
Immigrant Song	*Led Zeppelin*	*Led Zeppelin III*
Theme from Shaft	*Isaac Hayes*	*Shaft*
Fight the Power	*Public Enemy*	*Fear of a Black Planet*
In Your Eyes	*Peter Gabriel*	*So*
Bohemian Rhapsody	*Queen*	*A Night at the Opera*
You Never Can Tell	*Chuck Berry*	*St. Louis to Liverpool*
Don't You (Forget About Me)	*Simple Minds*	*The Breakfast Club*
Shallow	*Lady Gaga & Bradley Cooper*	*A Star is Born*
Old Time Rock and Roll	*Bob Seger*	*Stranger in Town*
The End	*The Doors*	*The Doors*
Kashmir	*Led Zeppelin*	*Physical Graffiti*
Stayin' Alive	*The Bee Gees*	*Saturday Night Fever*
The Bright Side of Life	*Monty Python*	*The Life of Brian*
I Will Always Love You	*Whitney Houston*	*The Bodyguard*
Eye of the Tiger	*Survivor*	*Rocky III/Eye of the Tiger*
Raindrops Keep Falling on My Head	*B.J. Thomas*	*Raindrops Keep Falling on My Head*

QUESTIONS

1. **Which was the first album to sell a million compact discs?**

   a. Dire Straits' *Brothers in Arms*
   b. The Police's *Synchronicity*
   c. Michael Jackson's *Thriller*
   d. Madonna's *Like a Virgin*

2. **Which garage rock staple started its life in the 1950s as a folk song (and was often listed as traditional) before it was covered by The Leaves, The Standells, Love, The Byrds, Jimi Hendrix, Patti Smith, and countless others?**

   a. Turn, Turn, Turn
   b. Hey Joe
   c. Gloria
   d. Dirty Water

3. **How many singles did Aretha Franklin have on the various Billboard charts?**

   a. 14
   b. 28
   c. 56
   d. 112

4. **What was the first song sung in Spanish to hit #1 in the US, doing so in 1987 as a movie with the same title came out?**

ANSWERS

1. **Dire Straits' *Brothers in Arms***

   It was #1 for nine weeks and has sold over 30 million copies. And don't forget that Sting gets co-writing credit for singing, "I Want My MTV" on "Money for Nothing."

   Recommended Album(s): *Brothers in Arms*

2. **"Hey Joe"**

   At the 1967 Monterey Pop Festival, David Crosby prefaced the Byrds' take on it by saying that someone was going to blow their version away later, knowing that Hendrix was waiting in the wings.

   Recommended Versions: Hendrix > Love > Standells > Patti Smith > Leaves > Byrds

3. **112 charting singles**

   Yeah, beat that. This includes 100 on the R&B charts and 17 top-ten pop singles. "Respect," "Chains of Fools," "Spanish Harlem," and "I Knew You Were Waiting (For Me)" are some of the top ones.

   Recommended Album(s): *Lady Soul*

4. **"La Bamba"**

   Richie Valens was the first to turn the Mexican folk song into a hit, but it wasn't until East LA band Los Lobos did it for his biopic that it hit #1.

   Recommended Album(s): Los Lobos' *Kiko* is good starting point.

1. **What was Ike & Tina Turner's highest charting single?**
   a. Nutbush City Limits
   b. A Fool in Love
   c. Proud Mary
   d. Sexy Ida

2. **Which Clash song is supposedly about Mick Jones' breakup with Ellen Foley (who also dueted on Meat Loaf's "Paradise by the Dashboard Light")?**
   a. Straight to Hell
   b. Know Your Rights
   c. Should I Stay or Should I Go?
   d. Train in Vain

3. **What beat novelist do 10,000 Maniacs sing a song to on their breakthrough album, *In My Tribe*?**
   a. Jack Kerouac
   b. Allen Ginsberg
   c. William S. Burroughs
   d. Gary Snyder

4. **What Childish Gambino song debuted at #1 in 2018, helped by the provocative and stunning music video directed by Hiro Murai?**

ANSWERS

1. **"Proud Mary"**

   Already a hit for Creedence Clearwater Revival two years earlier, it reached #4 in the US.

   Recommended Album(s): *Workin' Together* or any of Ike & Tina's live albums

2. **"Should I Stay Or Should I Go?"**

   Ellen Foley also played the public defender on the NBC sitcom, Night Court, before Markie Post took over—this is the sort of hardcore trivia you need to know!

   Recommended Album(s): *Combat Rock* is the album with the song, but when you've got a couple of hours let the glorious mess that is *Sandinista* roll over you.

3. **Jack Kerouac**

   Natalie Merchant and Robert Buck co-wrote "Hey Jack Kerouac" and "What's the Matter Here?," while Merchant gets solo credit for the album's other single, "Like the Weather."

   Recommended Album(s): *In My Tribe*

4. **"This Is America"**

   The video got over 12 million videos in the first 24 hours. Hiro Murai also directed several episodes of Donald Glover's *Atlanta*.

   Recommended Album(s): *3.15.20*

SUPERGROUPS

Jazz has lots of supergroups.

Coltrane and Monk and Miles and everyone would show up and work with each other. Those don't count. Partly because they're more supergroups in retrospect. At the time, it was often a famous bandleader with musicians who later became famous. A supergroup has to seem super at the time.

And it can't be just jammin'.

Powerhouse had Eric Clapton with Manfred Mann's Jack Bruce (before Bluesbreakers, before Cream) and the Spencer Davis Group's Steve Winwood (before Traffic), but they just spent one day in the studio. Also, Winwood was listed as Steve Anglo.

A supergroup needs to have people we already know who intentionally make an album as a band. The Rock Bottom Remainders are a supergroup because they have Stephen King, Matt Groening, Amy Tan, etc., and those are famous people. But I'm not asking about them because, as Dave Barry said, "We play music as well as Metallica writes novels."

On the next two pages, match the artist with the band(s) they came from and the supergroup they joined.

ORIGINAL BANDS	ARTISTS
The Yardbirds	David Crosby
Buffalo Springfield	Stephen Stills
Phish	Graham Nash
The Hollies	Neil Young
Primus	Tom Morello
The Byrds	Robert Palmer
The Spencer Davis Group	Eric Clapton
Cypress Hill	Trey Anastasio
Cream	Ginger Baker
Duran Duran	John & Andy Taylor
The Police	Chuck D
Public Enemy	Les Claypool
Rage Against the Machine	Steve Winwood
	Stewart Copeland
	B-Real

ARTISTS

David Crosby

Stephen Stills

Graham Nash

Neil Young

Tom Morello

Robert Palmer

Eric Clapton

Trey Anastasio

Ginger Baker

John & Andy Taylor

Chuck D

Les Claypool

Steve Winwood

Stewart Copeland

B-Real

SUPERGROUPS

Crosby, Stills, Nash & Young

Prophets of Rage

Oysterhead

Blind Faith

The Power Station

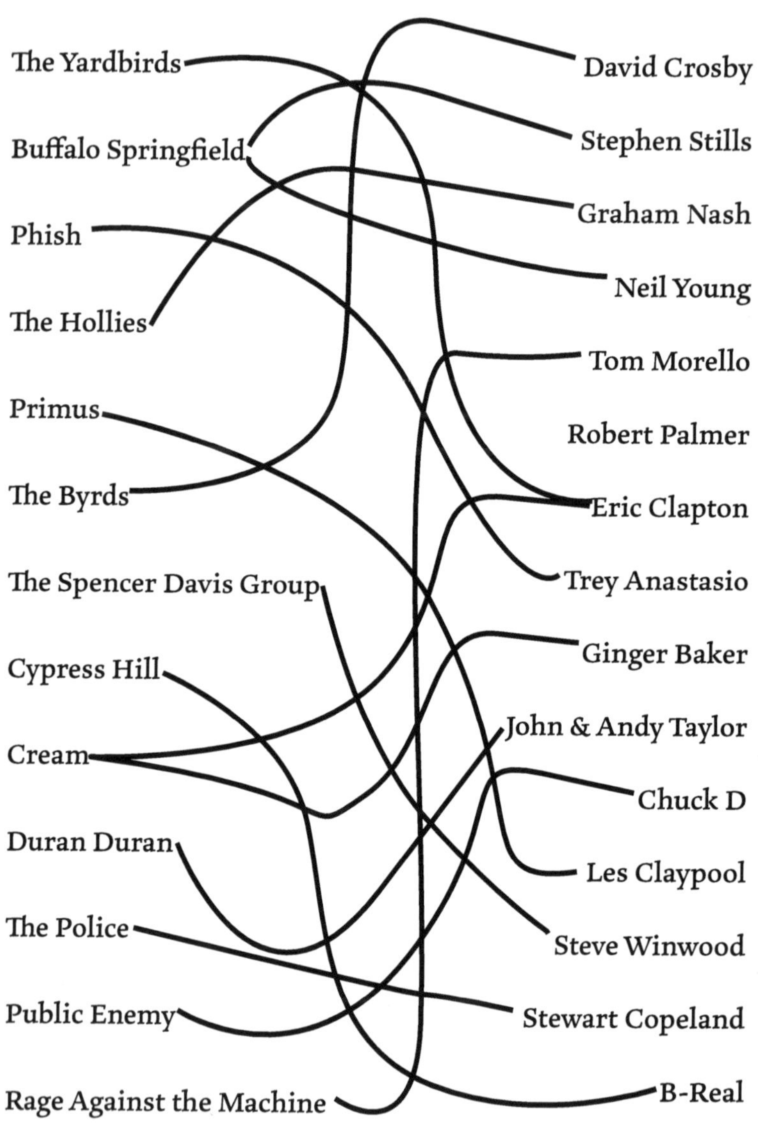
ORIGINAL BANDS
ARTISTS
The Yardbirds
Buffalo Springfield
Phish
The Hollies
Primus
The Byrds
The Spencer Davis Group
Cypress Hill
Cream
Duran Duran
The Police
Public Enemy
Rage Against the Machine
David Crosby
Stephen Stills
Graham Nash
Neil Young
Tom Morello
Robert Palmer
Eric Clapton
Trey Anastasio
Ginger Baker
John & Andy Taylor
Chuck D
Les Claypool
Steve Winwood
Stewart Copeland
B-Real

ARTISTS **SUPERGROUPS**

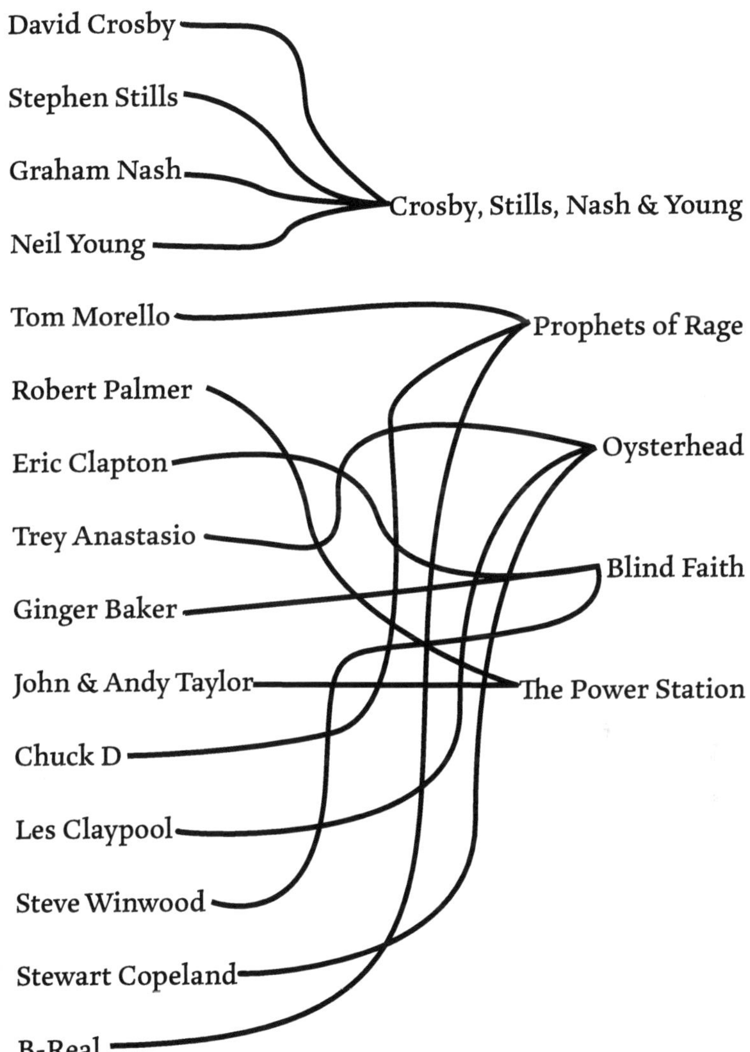
David Crosby
Stephen Stills
Graham Nash
Neil Young
Tom Morello
Robert Palmer
Eric Clapton
Trey Anastasio
Ginger Baker
John & Andy Taylor
Chuck D
Les Claypool
Steve Winwood
Stewart Copeland
B-Real
Crosby, Stills, Nash & Young
Prophets of Rage
Oysterhead
Blind Faith
The Power Station

SUPERGROUPS

Crosby, Stills, Nash & Young: The Byrds wouldn't let Crosby play his songs, Stills broke up Buffalo Springfield, and Nash thought the *Hollies Sing Dylan* trivialized Dylan. So, they formed a trio and then a quartet. **Early:** *Buffalo Springfield* (1966); The Byrds' *Mr. Tambourine Man* (1965); The Hollies' *Butterfly* (1967) **Late:** *Déjà Vu* (1970)

Prophets of Rage: Taking their name from the Public Enemy song, they spent 2016 on their "Make America Rage Again" Tour. **Early:** Public Enemy's *It Takes A Nation of Millions to Hold Us Back* (1988): Cypress Hill's *III: Temple of Doom* (1995); *Rage Against the Machine* (1992) **Late:** *Prophets of Rage* (2017)

Oysterhead: In 2000, Claypool needed a band for the New Orleans Jazz Fest and called up Anastasio and Copeland. Originally a one-time gig, they wrote new material and made it a real, if infrequent, band. **Early:** The Police's *Synchronicity* (1983); Phish's *A Live One* (1995); Primus' *Sailing the Seas of Cheese* (1991) **Late:** *The Grand Pecking Order* (2001)

Blind Faith: Clapton and Winwood started jamming in 1969, after Cream and Traffic (momentarily) broke up. They wanted to distance themselves from their earlier bands, but kept dipping into those catalogues which disillusioned them. **Early:** The Yardbirds' *For Your Love* (1965); *The Best of the Spencer Davis Group Featuring Steve Winwood* (1967); Cream's *Wheels of Fire* (1968); Traffic's *Traffic* **Late:** *Blind Faith* (1969)

The Power Station: Duran Duran's Taylor brothers were big fans of Palmer and when they went on hiatus, they asked him to join them to make some rock 'n' roll. **Early:** Duran Duran's *Rio* (1982); Robert Palmer's *Sneakin' Sally Through the Alley* (1974) **Late:** *The Power Station* (1985)

QUESTIONS

1. **Which Ed Sheeran song holds the record for the longest at #1 (twelve weeks)?**
   a. Shape of You
   b. Galway Girl
   c. Perfect
   d. I Don't Care

2. **Which LA DJ, the Mayor of Sunset Strip, helped artists on the cusp from David Bowie to Hole?**
   a. Jim Ladd
   b. Murray the K
   c. Rodney on the Roq
   d. Acid Cat

3. **When introducing which band in 1992 did Eric Clapton claim that their 1968 debut album changed both his life and the course of American music?**
   a. Love
   b. The Doors
   c. The Flying Burrito Brothers
   d. The Band

4. **Three of the top ten selling albums of all time are soundtracks to movies, two from the 1970s and one from the 1990s. What are they?**

ANSWERS

1. **"Shape of You"**

   While +, *X*, ÷, and = are all great album titles, as a former math teacher, I'm most excited for when he starts hitting calculus.

   Recommended Album(s): +

2. **Rodney on the Roq**

   He helped Bowie gain a foothold in America, owned a nightclub or two, and spun the music he loved on KROQ in Los Angeles for over 30 years. And was an occasional stand-in for Davey Jones on *The Monkees.*

   Recommended Album(s): I've got a tape somewhere from when I was a kid where he played a bunch of his early Bowie bootlegs. Come on by and I'll try to find it.

3. **The Band**

   And you can make a pretty strong case that he was right.

   Recommended Album(s): *Music from Big Pink*

4. ***The Bodyguard, Saturday Night Fever,* and *Grease***

   They sold 45, 42, and 38 million, respectively. *Dirty Dancing* also makes the top twenty.

   Recommended Album(s): Well, those albums

SCRAMBLED ALBUMS

Can you decode the classic albums below?

Frightening Heather Dies

This hip hop trio named their debut album after a Johnny Cash tune, even though the movie *Heathers* came out the same year.

Britney Sickle

Britney Spears' debut came out a year after this album, so it's just as well the band didn't use this name. Although the attorney who put Britney under her conservatorship tried the same with this band's leader.

Fake, Dishonored Tom

This 1973 album dealt with mental health amongst other issues, so maybe Tom was code for Syd?

A Virile King

Could it be about Sean Penn? Guy Ritchie? We can't say.

SCRAMBLED ALBUMS

Frightening Heather Dies
Three Feet High and Rising

De La Soul: 1989
Coming out amidst a surge of gangsta rap, this album is credited with helping to start alternative hip hop.

Britney Sickle
Celebrity Skin

Hole: 1998
Celebrity Skin was Courtney Love & Hole's third album and included the hits "Malibu" and "Awful."

Fake, Dishonored Tom
Dark Side of the Moon

Pink Floyd: 1998
The album charted for 957 weeks. It sold *45 million copies*. My god.

A Virile King
Like a Virgin

Madonna: 1984
The first album by a woman to sell 5 million units in the US.

QUESTIONS

1. **Who is the Boss referring to in "Tenth Avenue Freeze Out," when he says that "the Big Man joined the band"?**
    a. Jimmy Carter
    b. Little Steven
    c. Clarence Clemons
    d. Isaac Hayes

2. **Who played the space alien star of the 1976 film, *The Man Who Fell to Earth*?**
    a. Mick Jagger
    b. Boy George
    c. Liam Gallagher
    d. David Bowie

3. **As a promotion for what artist did MTV purchase a house across from a toxic waste dump in 1984 for $20,000?**
    a. John Cougar Mellencamp
    b. Bruce Springsteen
    c. Michael Jackson
    d. Paula Abdul

4. **What artist had four #1 singles from his 2004 album, *Confessions*?**

ANSWERS

1. **Clarence Clemons**

   When saxophonist Clarence Clemons first met Bruce Springsteen in Asbury Park, the Big Man opened the front door and it literally flew off the hinges. A sign of things to come.

   Recommended Album(s): *Born to Run*

2. **David Bowie**

   Who else? Bowie later wrote the musical *Lazarus* as a sequel to this film (while he was secretly dying) using new and old songs.

   Recommended Album(s): *Lazarus*

3. **John Cougar Mellencamp**

   Once they realized it was across from the dump, they bought another one before painting it pink (ya know, "Pink Houses") and awarded it to a lucky fan. It took them eight years to get rid of the toxic one.

   Recommended Album(s): *Uh-Huh*

4. **Usher**

   "Yeah," "Burn," "Confessions Part II," and "My Boo" all hit the top stop, while "Caught Up" stalled at #8.

   Recommended Album(s): *Confessions*

SEATTLE VS. ATHENS

There was a thriving music scene around the University of Georgia in Athens in the late 1970s and 1980s. Then again, what kind of a loser college town doesn't have a thriving music scene? But somehow the intersection of country, southern rock, and bluegrass after the 40 Watt Club opened on Halloween night in 1978 gave this scene more legs. Pretty soon, Athens was giving quirky bands across the country something to aim for.

There was never anything quirky about the Seattle scene; all right, Lois could be quirky at times, but I'm talking about grunge here. The word was first used in 1987 to describe Green River's second ep, before they broke up and went on to form bands like Mudhoney and Pearl Jam. A rather vague term, grunge has a lot of distorted guitars (usually) and angsty, introspective lyrics. Grunge bands hate the term because they are too angsty and introspective.

SEATTLE GRUNGE

1. **Which Nirvana member went on to lead the Foo Fighters?**
   a. Krist Novoselic
   b. Dave Grohl
   c. Kurt Cobain
   d. Chad Channing

2. **Which Pearl Jam album managed to reach the charts for two weeks while it was still just released on vinyl?**
   a. *Vs.*
   b. *Ten*
   c. *Vitalogy*
   d. *No Exit*

3. **The song, "Touch Me, I'm Dick," by fictional band Citizen Dick as seen in the grunge-era Seattle movie *Singles*, is a reference to which band?**
   a. Mudhoney
   b. Green River
   c. Screaming Trees
   d. Temple of the Dog

4. **What band was Chris Cornell the singer and rhythm guitarist for?**

THE ATHENS SCENE

1. **Which R.E.M. song, recorded July 8, 1981 by Mitch Easter, gave college radio its smugness for the rest of the decade?**
   a. Stand
   b. Driver 8
   c. (Don't Go Back to) Rockville
   d. Radio Free Europe

2. **What alt.country band, originating in Athens in the 1990s, has consisted of Patterson Hood & Mike Cooley (continuously) and Jason Isbell & Shona Tucker (for a few albums)?**
   a. The Jody Grind
   b. Drive-By Truckers
   c. The Bottle Rockets
   d. The Vandoliers

3. **Who went from being a University of Georgia DJ to releasing *The Grey Album*, forming Gnarls Barkley with CeeLo Green, and joining with the Shins to become Broken Bells?**
   a. DJ Spooky
   b. Danger Mouse
   c. André 3000
   d. Jemini

4. **What 1989 song, topping out at #3, was inspired by the Hawaiian Ha-Le Club and its tin roof?**

SEATTLE GRUNGE

1. **Dave Grohl**

   Grohl was a drummer for Nirvana and, while he always had his guitar with him, he said he was usually too intimidated to play his own songs.

   Recommended Album(s): *Foo Fighters*

2. ***Vitalogy***

   Pearl Jam's 1994 release sold 34,000 lps in its first week and 877,000 cds the first week that format was available. The lead single was, appropriately, "Spin the Black Circle."

   Recommended Album(s): *Vitalogy*

3. **Mudhoney**

   Mudhoney's 1988 college radio hit, "Touch Me, I'm Sick," helped put the Sub Pop label on the map. At least the college radio map.

   Recommended Album(s): *Superfuzz Bigmuff*

4. **Soundgarden**

   Cornell also fronted Temple of the Dog which was formed in tribute to his former roommate, the late Andrew Wood of Mother Love Bone.

   Recommended Album(s): *Superunknown*

1. **Radio Free Europe**

   And well deservedly so. College radio gave R.E.M. a foothold to conquer the world. In 1996, Warner Brothers gave them the largest contract ever at the time, for $80 million.

   Recommended Album(s): *Murmur*

2. **Drive-By Truckers**

   Featuring multiple top-notch songwriters and guitarists, as well as plenty of attitude, the Truckers have been critics' darlings and just small enough to still be cool. They also have Muscle Shoals in their blood.

   Recommended Album(s): *Southern Rock Opera, Brighter Than Creation's Dark*

3. **Danger Mouse**

   The *Grey Album* mixed Jay-Z's *The Black Album* and the Beatles' White Album. Danger Mouse has won six Grammys, covering urban, alternative, non-classical, and rock genres and was part of winning Album of the Year for Adele's *25*.

   Recommended Album(s): *The Grey Album,* Gnarls Barkley's *St. Elsewhere*

4. **"Love Shack"**

   The music stopped as they were recording, but Cindy Wilson just kept singing: "Tin roof, rusted."

   Recommended Album(s): *Cosmic Thing*

WINNER: SEATTLE

Athens had the advantage going in, judging the whole area versus just grunge in Seattle. So I decided to add Jimi Hendrix onto that side of the scale and Seattle won. Also, they throw fish at Pike Place and that's pretty cool.

Besides, Athens is okay with having its moment in time. The hipsters are just glad someone's talking about something besides football.

1. **Most of the Eagles started off as members of whose backing band?**
   a. Mike Nesmith
   b. Linda Ronstadt
   c. Jackson Browne
   d. Stephen Stills

2. **Which album was released as a response to Marvin Gaye's album, *What's Going On*?**
   a. *Ain't That Good News*
   b. *Where I'm Coming From*
   c. *There's a Riot Goin' On*
   d. *Are You Experienced?*

3. **YouTube stars, TwinsthenewTrend went viral during the Covid pandemic for their reaction to which song's drum fill?**
   a. Rush's "Tom Sawyer"
   b. Phil Collins' "In the Air Tonight"
   c. The White Stripes' "Seven Nation Army"
   d. Led Zeppelin's "Moby Dick"

4. **What artist had a song reach #1 on the charts, three weeks after he died in 1980?**

ANSWERS

1. **Linda Ronstadt**

   Perfecting their California sound with her, the Eagles went out on their own in 1972.

   Recommended Album(s): *Eagles*

2. ***There's a Riot Goin' On***

   Technically, the album wasn't a response, but Sly & the Family Stone retitled it from *Africa Talks to You*, to answer Gaye's question. It went to #1, as did "Family Affair" on the singles chart. Get it.

   Recommended Album(s): *There's a Riot Goin' On*

3. **Phil Collins' "In the Air Tonight"**

   The urban myth is he wrote it after seeing someone not assist a drowning victim. The truth is that the drums are still astounding.

   Recommended Album(s): *Face Value*

4. **John Lennon**

   Lennon called "(Just Like) Starting Over" his Elvis/Orbison track.

   Recommended Album(s): *Double Fantasy*

BRITISH BLUES ROCK

Fill in the names in the following paragraph.

In 1962, 14-year-old __________(A) joined his brother in the Spencer Davis Group, playing organ and singing. A year later, guitarist ________ (B) left the Roosters and joined the Yardbirds. He was there for a year and a half before deciding they were getting too pop, so he skipped and began his blues tutelage in John Mayall's Bluesbreakers. Soon after, bassist _________ (C) joined them, having left the Graham Bond Organisation. Meanwhile, the Yardbirds found a new guitarist in ______ ______ (D) and in 1966 added another guitarist in session man ________ ______ (E). In 1965, (C) left the Bluesbreakers and played bass for Manfred Mann for a year, while bassist _________ (F) (re)joined the Bluesbreakers. Guitarist (B) then left the Bluesbreakers (to be replaced by _________ (G)) and formed Cream with (C) and drummer ______ ______ (H), also from the Graham Bond Organisation. (A) left Spencer Davis and formed Traffic. Second Yardbirds guitarist (D) then formed his own group with __________ (I) on vocals and _______ (J) on bass, while __________ (K) joined the Bluesbreakers on drums. (E) had to fill concert dates for the Yardbirds, so formed a new band, called Led Zeppelin. (FG&K) then left the Bluesbreakers to form Fleetwood Mac, forcing John Mayall to bring in guitarist ___________ (L), who had first met Mayall at the age of 16, when he volunteered from the crowd to cover for a missing (B). In 1969, (I&J) left (D)'s band, to turn Small Faces into Faces, retaining ________ (M) on drums, while (L) left the Bluesbreakers for the Rolling Stones, and (B&H) left Cream to form Blind Faith with (A), during a Traffic interlude. Finally, in the mid-1970s, (J) replaced (L) in the Rolling Stones and (H) became the drummer for the Who.

BRITISH BLUES ROCK

In 1962, 14-year-old **Steve Winwood** (A) joined his brother in the Spencer Davis Group, playing organ and singing. A year later, guitarist **Eric Clapton** (B) left the Roosters and joined the Yardbirds. He was there for a year and a half before deciding they were getting too pop, so he skipped and began his blues tutelage in John Mayall's Bluesbreakers. Soon after, bassist **Jack Bruce** (C) joined them, having left the Graham Bond Organisation. Meanwhile, the Yardbirds found a new guitarist in **Jeff Beck** (D) and in 1966 added another guitarist in session man **Jimmy Page** (E). In 1965, (C) left the Bluesbreakers and played bass for Manfred Mann for a year, while bassist **John McVie** (F) (re)joined the Bluesbreakers. Guitarist (B) then left the Bluesbreakers (to be replaced by **Peter Green** (G)) and formed Cream with (C) and drummer **Ginger Baker** (H), also from the Graham Bond Organisation. (A) left Spencer Davis and formed Traffic. Second Yardbirds guitarist (D) then formed his own group with **Rod Stewart** (I) on vocals and **Ron Wood** (J) on bass, while **Mick Fleetwood** (K) joined the Bluesbreakers on drums. (E) had to fill concert dates for the Yardbirds, so formed a new band, called Led Zeppelin. (FG&K) then left the Bluesbreakers to form Fleetwood Mac, forcing John Mayall to bring in guitarist **Mick Taylor** (L), who had first met Mayall at the age of 16, when he volunteered from the crowd to cover for a missing (B). In 1969, (I&J) left (D)'s band, to turn Small Faces into Faces, retaining **Kenney Jones** (M) on drums, while (L) left the Bluesbreakers for the Rolling Stones, and (B&H) left Cream to form Blind Faith with (A), during a Traffic interlude. Finally, in the mid-1970s, (J) replaced (L) in the Rolling Stones and (H) became the drummer for the Who.

1. **Which one-time homeless, anti-folk singer in Los Angeles originally thought his rapping skills made him a total loser?**
    a. Eminem
    b. Childish Gambino
    c. Beck
    d. Chuck D

2. **What was the name of Kate Bush's 1985 album, her biggest, which featured "Running Up That Hill (A Deal with God)"?**
    a. *Hounds of Love*
    b. *The Dreaming*
    c. *The Whole Story*
    d. *The Sensual World*

3. **Which Commodores' song did Clyde Orange sing lead on, because it was decided that usual lead singer Lionel Richie's voice wasn't funky enough?**
    a. Still
    b. Brick House
    c. Three Times a Lady
    d. Slippery When Wet

4. **What Fatboy Slim song did Spike Jonze direct the music video for and star in as part of a dance troupe in front of a movie theater in Westwood, CA?**

ANSWERS

1. **Beck**

   He was trying to sound like Chuck D, but was unhappy with it, so made up some lyrics about being a "loser" and his career took off.

   Recommended Album(s): *Mellow Gold*

2. ***Hounds of Love***

   In 2020, Rolling Stone named it the 68th best album of all time.

   Recommended Album(s): *Hounds of Love*

3. **"Brick House"**

   During a break in the studio, the bassist started jamming and everyone joined in, one by one. They liked it and everyone was instructed to go home and write lyrics to go with it. William King's wife, Shirley Hanna-King, came up with the winning song.

   Recommended Album(s): *Commodores*

4. **"Praise You"**

   In 1996 ex-Housemartins bassist Norman Cook changed his name to Fatboy Slim and led the Big Beat movement. In the US, he got the most attention for this song, helped by the video which cost $800 to film guerilla-style, featuring an annoyed theater employee turning the boombox off halfway through.

   Recommended Album(s): *You've Come a Long Way Baby*

MADONNA VS. PRINCE

These two artists owned the 1980s. And a lot of the ensuing decades.

She landed in New York in 1978 with $35 in her pocket and has ended up selling more than 300 million records, the most for a female artist. On top of that she has grossed a billion and half dollars from concert tickets.

Two months older than Madonna, Prince released his first album in 1978, but started hitting his stride with Controversy *and* 1999 *at the start of the 1980s. He released 39 albums during his lifetime (to the tune of 150 million records sold), but left dozens of albums unreleased in his vaults. He lent many of his songs to other artists and estimates for the number he wrote run as high as a thousand.*

MADONNA

1. **In which music video did Madonna strike poses of Veronica Lake, Jean Harlow, Marlene Dietrich, and others?**
    a. Superstar
    b. Lucky Star
    c. Erotica
    d. Vogue

2. **Which Madonna song was the first by a major artist to be featured in a commercial before being released to radio stations?**
    a. Like a Virgin
    b. Like a Prayer
    c. La Isla Bonita
    d. Erotica

3. **Which film based on an Andrew Lloyd Webber musical featured Madonna?**
    a. *Jesus Christ Superstar*
    b. *Bloodhounds of Broadway*
    c. *Evita*
    d. *Cats*

4. **What Chic guitarist produced Madonna's "Like a Virgin," as well as songs from David Bowie ("Let's Dance"), Duran Duran ("Notorious"), Daft Punk ("Get Lucky"), and many, many others?**

1. **What tv show was Prince on when he told the security bear that he was "The Artist Formerly Known as Prince," to receive the reply: "and I'm the bear currently known as not amused"?**
    a. *Greg and Dharma*
    b. *Magnum PI*
    c. *The Lehrer News Hour*
    d. *Muppets Tonight*

2. **What was Prince's birth name?**
    a. Prince
    b. Roger
    c. Billie
    d. Otis

3. **Which of these songs did Prince not write?**
    a. Love Song (Madonna)
    b. Stand Back (Stevie Nicks)
    c. Manic Monday (Bangles)
    d. Nothing Compares 2U (Sinead O'Connor)

4. **At one point in 1984, Prince had the top album, single, and film in the US with what three works?**

MADONNA

1. **"Vogue"**

   As well as Marilyn Monroe, Bette Davis, Judy Garland... It's always near the top of greatest music videos ever lists.

   Recommended Album(s): *I'm Breathless*

2. **"Like a Prayer"**

   She got a $5 million deal and issued an upbeat commercial with her 8-year old self dancing. THEN, after 250 million people saw it, she released her official video of the song with interracial kissing and co-opting lots of religious imagery. Pepsi dropped its endorsement to appease those irate with it but already seemed cool just for being associated with her (she kept the fee).

   Recommended Album(s): *Like a Prayer*

3. ***Evita***

   The film made $151 million, and Madonna got strong reviews. Plus, "You Must Love Me" won the Oscar for Best Original Song.

   Recommended Album(s): *Evita*

4. **Niles Rodgers**

   Chic plays live and sometimes seems like the best wedding band ever, except all the "cover" songs are ones Rodgers helped make.

   Recommended Album(s): *Like a Virgin*

1. ***Muppets Tonight***

   Nice to see Prince's sense of humor coming through, even doing Hee Haw jokes in a cornfield with an alligator.

   Recommended Album(s): WRITE DISNEY AND HAVE THEM RELEASE MUPPETS TONIGHT!

2. **Prince (Prince Rogers Nelson)**

   His father's stage name in the jazz combo he had with his wife was Prince Rogers and he said he wanted his son to excel beyond what he did. But a young Prince asked that people call him Skipper.

   Recommended Album(s): *Lovesexy*

3. **"Stand Back" (sorta)**

   In 1983, after Stevie Nicks got married, she and her husband drove up to Santa Barbara for their honeymoon. "Little Red Corvette" came on the radio and she started humming. The couple picked up a tape recorder and made a demo that night (add your own innuendo). Once she got to the studio, she called up Prince, told him the story, and he came over and played uncredited synthesizers on it. They also decided to split the publishing rights on it.

   Recommended Album(s): *1999*

4. ***Purple Rain,* "When Doves Cry," *Purple Rain***

   The album sold 25 million copies and the film made ten times its $7 million budget.

   Recommended Album(s): *Purple Rain*

WINNER: PRINCE

This was a tough one. Prince had the Muppets, but Madonna had the kiss with Britney Spears and Christina Aguilera. So the tiebreaker has to go to the Super Bowl halftime shows. And I've got nothing against her set, but Prince doing "Purple Rain," with the rain falling around him pushes him over the top.

1. **Who cut an electric version of "House of the Rising Sun," after hearing a young Dylan's acoustic take, making (arguably) the first folk rock song?**
   a. Peter, Paul & Mary
   b. The Animals
   c. The Byrds
   d. War

2. **What T. Rex song, named after a vehicle, did Marc Bolan's label release without his permission after he left them?**
   a. REO Speedwagon
   b. Metal Guru
   c. Jeepster
   d. GTO

3. **Whom did Kanye West interrupt on stage at the 2015 Grammys to protest that Beyoncé should have won Album of the Year instead?**
   a. Justin Timberlake
   b. Arcade Fire
   c. Beck
   d. Taylor Swift

4. **In the closing track of Warren Zevon's *Excitable Boy*, what does the singer need sent, since the "shit has hit the fan"?**

ANSWERS

1. **The Animals**

   Lead Animal Eric Burdon later formed the band War and had a hit with "Spill the Wine."

   Recommended Album(s): *The Animals,* but find a compilation to capture their changing sounds.

2. **"Jeepster"**

   T. Rex's glam rock stunner from 1971 was produced by Tony Visconti, frequent David Bowie producer.

   Recommended Album(s): *Electric Warrior*

3. **Beck**

   Beck also had thought Beyoncé was going to win, but didn't give the trophy back. Kanye had done the same thing in 2009 when Taylor Swift won the MTV Best Female Video award.

   Recommended Album(s): *Morning Phase* was the album in question, but I might also recommend 1999's *Midnite Vultures* (or 1996's *Odelay,* if you want the hits).

4. **Lawyers, guns, and money**

   Rick Derringer did a cover of it in 1978. And made some odd choices on it. Just listen to it. Once.

   Recommended Album(s): Warren Zevon's *Excitable Boy*

1. **Who had the first album in the Christian category to go platinum, with over a million units sold?**
   a. Jars of Clay
   b. Stryper
   c. Amy Grant
   d. Sam Phillips

2. **What was the first song sung (partially) in German, to hit #1 in the US, in 1986?**
   a. Rock Me Amadeus (Falco)
   b. 99 Luft Balloons (Nena)
   c. Tago Mago (Can)
   d. Autobahn (Kraftwerk)

3. **What was the name of Elvis Costello's highest charting single, which he co-wrote with Paul McCartney?**
   a. Veronica
   b. Alison
   c. Watching the Detectives
   d. (The Angels Wanna Wear My) Red Shoes

4. **In 2006, Damon Albarn of Blur, Paul Simonon of the Clash, and Simon Tong of the Verve formed what royal-tinged, spaghetti western band?**

ANSWERS

1. **Amy Grant**

   1982's *Age to Age* was her fourth album and set the stage for the Contemporary Christian genre.

   Recommended Album(s): *Age to Age*

2. **Rock Me Amadeus (Falco)**

   It was inspired by the movie, *Amadeus* and, well, Amadeus himself. Their other big international hit was "Der Kommisar."

   Recommended Album(s): *Falco 3*

3. **"Veronica"**

   Costello and McCartney wrote several songs together, including "My Brave Face" from McCartney's *Flowers in the Dirt.*

   Recommended Album(s): *Spike*

4. **The Good, the Bad & the Queen**

   Okay, technically they claimed the band had no name and that was just the name of album, but I'm not going to make you try to stream a band with no name.

   Recommended Album(s): *The Good, the Bad & the Queen*

IRISH VS. SCOTTISH MUSIC

The terms "Irish Music" and "Scottish Music" are about as useful as "American Music." This is to say, not at all. While traditional Irish and Scottish music have strong identities that permeate other genres, I'm concentrating here on rock. Which isn't that useful a term either.

Hailed as the UK's answer to Dylan, mid-1960s Donovan brought a Scottish undercurrent to his music, mixing Celtic rock with folk, jazz, and a bit of calypso. Meanwhile, Jack Bruce was mixing blues and jazz, for the Bluesbreakers and Cream. The 1970s saw "tartan teen sensations," the Bay City Rollers hit it big, and a few punk bands (the Exploited, the Rezillos), before the 1980s exploded with Simple Minds, Annie Lennox, the Jesus and Mary Chain, Big Country, and the Proclaimers. Belle and Sebastian and Camera Obscura followed with Franz Ferdinand, KT Tunstall, Frightened Rabbit and Glasvegas emerging in the 21st Century.

Ireland in the 1960s, saw Van Morrison's Them crack a few hits, while Rory Gallagher's bluesy Taste seemed poised for the big time. Thin Lizzy came along and the Boomtown Rats straddled the pub/punk rock line, before relocating to London, while Stiff Little Fingers stayed on the punk side. U2 set an impossibly high standard for all Irish bands, although many would say the same for (Anglo-Irish) band the Pogues—at least my friends would argue that. Sinead O'Connor, the Corrs, and the Cranberries became stars in the 1980s and 1990s.

IRISH ARTISTS

1. **What Pogues' song has hit the UK Christmas chart in almost 20 different years?**
   a. The Turkish Song of the Damned
   b. Thousands are Sailing
   c. Fairytale of New York
   d. White Christmas

2. **What band was originally called the Feedback and the Hype?**
   a. U2
   b. Thin Lizzy
   c. The Waterboys
   d. The Cranberries

3. **Bob Geldof named his band The Boomtown Rats after reading whose autobiography, *Bound for Glory*?**
   a. Billie Holliday
   b. Woody Guthrie
   c. Josh White
   d. Muddy Waters

4. **What was Enya's 1988 breakthrough single?**

1. **Which Donovan song supposedly had the FBI worried that hippies were smoking banana skins?**
    a. Catch the Wind
    b. Goo Goo Barabajagal
    c. Mellow Yellow
    d. Jennifer Juniper

2. **Aretha Franklin shared vocals on which 1985 Eurythmics song?**
    a. Missionary Man
    b. Here Comes the Rain Again
    c. Sisters Are Doin' It for Themselves
    d. Sweet Dreams (Are Made of These)

3. **Who sang on "Throw the 'R' Away": "I'm just going to have to hesitate, to make sure my words on your Saxon ears don't grate"?**
    a. The Proclaimers
    b. The Bay City Rollers
    c. Big Country
    d. Camera Obscura

4. **What band recorded their first album as part of a music business course at Glasgow's Stow College in 1994?**

IRISH ARTISTS

1. **"Fairytale of New York"**

   A much loved classic, it should be noted that the version from *A Jon Bon Jovi Christmas* was called one of the worst songs of 2020.

   Recommended Album(s): *If I Should Fall From Grace with God*

2. **U2**

   U2 was a US Air Force plane, famous for when Gary Powers was shot down in 1960 by the Soviet Union while on a CIA mission.

   Recommended Album(s): *Joshua Tree*

3. **Woody Guthrie**

   Bound for Glory is a (mostly) autobiographical take on Guthrie's travels, riding the trains across the country.

   Recommended Album(s): *The Fine Art of Surfacing* is the only album that all of my siblings bought separately growing up. You should have it too.

4. **"Orinoco Flow"**

   The Orinoco is a major river in South America, although the title is more directly from Orinoco Studios, where the song was recorded.

   Recommended Album(s): *Watermark*

1. **"Mellow Yellow"**

   It was actually about a vibrator, so try to put that in your pipe and smoke it.

   Recommended Album(s): I'd say go for *Fairytale,* but one of his best-of compilations will you get this and more of his hits.

2. **"Sisters Are Doin' It for Themselves"**

   Annie Lennox was trying to write a feminist anthem that could get played on the radio. Which made Aretha an obvious choice. A few of Tom Petty's Heartbreakers back them up.

   Recommended Album(s): *Be Yourself Tonight*

3. **The Proclaimers**

   It opened their first album, *This Is the Story,* in 1987. They didn't get much traction in the US until the film *Benny & Joon* highlighted "I'm Gonna Be (500 Miles)" off their second album.

   Recommended Album(s): *This Is the Story, Sunshine on Leith*

4. **Belle and Sebastian**

   Usually they just did a single each year, but Belle and Sebastian had so many good songs, they let them record a full album in three days.

   Recommended Album(s): *Tigermilk*

WINNER: IRELAND

Going in, I was rooting for Scotland, but Ireland just overwhelmed them. As good as Belle and Sebastian and Franz Ferdinand are, Ireland's got U2 in its collective pocket and can whip out the Cranberries and the Pogues as needed. And the Boomtown Rats and Sinead. Yet I find myself clicking on Indie Scottish radio more often. So the vote may change tomorrow.

1. **What was the name of Sheryl Crow's first album?**
   a. *Tuesday Night Music Club*
   b. *Sheryl Crow*
   c. *Dookie*
   d. *The Globe Sessions*

2. **Members of Jethro Tull, Pink Floyd, Genesis, and Led Zeppelin helped finance which movie?**
   a. *Monty Python and the Holy Grail*
   b. *The Rocky Horror Picture Show*
   c. *The Wall*
   d. *Caligula*

3. **What Flying Burrito Brother was hanging out so much with Keith Richards during the *Exile on Main Street* sessions that Mick Jagger worried about Keith's well-being?**
   a. Gram Parsons
   b. Chris Hillman
   c. Roger McGuinn
   d. Don Henley

4. **What was Bad Company's Paul Rodger's first major band, whose big hit was "All Right Now"?**

ANSWERS

1. ***Tuesday Night Music Club***

   She wrote most of the songs with her music club, which met on, uh, Tuesday nights. When "All I Wanna Do" hit it big, there were some disagreements on songwriting credit.

   Recommended Album(s): *Tuesday Night Music Club.* I drove from Maine to Santa Monica Boulevard in 1994 in a car with no cd/tape deck and lost count of how many times I heard that song on the radio.

2. ***Monty Python and the Holy Grail***

   Supposedly it seemed a good tax write-off at the time. Thirty years later, they were still receiving dividends when *Spamalot* hit Broadway.

   Recommended Album(s): *The Album of the Soundtrack of the Trailer of the Film of Monty Python and the Holy Grail.* It wasn't just David Bowie and Pixies albums I listened to growing up.

3. **Gram Parsons**

   Keith and Gram were big fans of Merle Haggard and of heroin. Both can lead to trouble.

   Recommended Album(s): Gram's *Grievous Angel,* the Rolling Stone's *Exile on Main Street* ain't bad either.

4. **Free**

   The band sold more than 20 million albums! And I love this song, but I can't remember anything else they did.

   Recommended Album(s): I think, maybe, just find this song? Or let me know if there's more that I should listen to? John Mayall just released 35 hours of new tapes, so that's kinda taking up my time.

SCRAMBLED ALBUMS

Can you decode the classic albums below?

Screaming Coriander

When this country icon teamed up with a famed hip hop producer, perhaps they should have gone full punk and chosen this title.

When Gretchen Masturbate?

This album ignited the East Coast Renaissance of hip hop and would have, even if Gretchen masturbated 36 times.

Pretested Manhood

You could say he pretested manhood with his first band, Mudcrutch, before hitting it big with this lp.

Unembellished Ted Cookin'!

This 45-track post-punk/hardcore/funk/country/whaddygot album sold literally thousands of copies.

SCRAMBLED ALBUMS

Screaming Coriander
American Recordings

Johnny Cash: 1994

Rick Rubin helped remake Johnny Cash for a new generation.

When Gretchen Masturbate?
Enter the Wu-Tang (36 Chambers)

Wu-Tang Clan: 1993

The Wu-Tang Clan had nine members, each with four chambers in their heart, for a total of 36. Or it might have something to do with Bruce Lee.

Pretested Manhood
Damn the Torpedoes

Tom Petty and the Heartbreakers: 1979

It was #2 for 7 weeks but hit a wall called *The Wall.*

Unembellished Ted Cookin'!
Double Nickels on the Dime

The Minutemen: 1984

The boys from San Pedro hit a tragic end before they had a chance to hit it big. (Spoiler: they were too econo to hit it big.)

1. **What 150+ million album singer did the San Diego Padres sign to a minor league contract in 1999?**
    a. Garth Brooks
    b. Jay-Z
    c. Dwight Yoakam
    d. Jennifer Lopez

2. **Which rocker supposedly spent much of 1976 subsiding on peppers, cocaine, and milk?**
    a. Gary Glitter
    b. Keith Richards
    c. David Bowie
    d. Iggy Pop

3. **The 2005 Live 8 Concerts featured the first performance in 24 years of the most famous lineup of which band?**
    a. Pink Floyd
    b. Boomtown Rats
    c. Queen
    d. AC/DC

4. **Liz Phair's *Exile in Guyville* was a response to what classic album?**

ANSWERS

1. **Garth Brooks**

   Garth ended up with a .045 average and was not invited to the Show. The New York Mets and Kansas City Royals also gave him a shot, but he sadly had to give up on his dreams. Oh, well.

   Recommended Album(s): *No Fences.* Yo La Tengo also does a version of "Meet the Mets" on *Yo La Tengo Is Murdering the Classics,* if that helps.

2. **David Bowie**

   He lost 100 pounds and was never able to explain how he made *Station to Station.*

   Recommended Album(s): *Station to Station*

3. **Pink Floyd**

   Live 8 were ten concerts around the world in July 2005 to support anti-poverty initiatives, on the 20th anniversary of Live Aid. And while Syd Barrett justly has his admirers, he's not officially part of the classic line-up (as dictated by this book).

   Recommended Album(s): The Live 8 DVD set has 120 tracks over four discs.

4. **The Rolling Stones' *Exile on Main Street***

   Many critics at the time didn't like the Stones' lp (they have changed their minds since), but they all loved Phair's response.

   Recommended Album(s): Both albums are classics and available in expanded versions.

SONGS TO BOOKS

Rock artists want to make sure that everyone knows they can read. And not just comic books, but books without pictures. On the following pages match the book with the the artist who sang about it.

BOOKS	BANDS
Wuthering Heights (Emily Brontë)	The Police
Alice in Wonderland (Lewis Carrol)	Jefferson Airplane
Sirens of Titan (Kurt Vonnegut)	Kate Bush
Lolita (Vladimir Nabokov)	Lou Reed
Romeo and Juliet (William Shakespeare)	Iron Maiden
Lord of the Rings (JRR Tolkien)	Al Stewart
The Diary of Anne Frank	Red Hot Chili Peppers
Yertle the Turtle (Dr. Seuss)	Led Zeppelin
Perfume (Patrick Süskind)	Nirvana
The Rime of the Ancient Mariner (Samuel Taylor Coleridge)	Neutral Milk Hotel

BANDS	BOOKS
Venus in Furs (Leopol von Sacher-Masoch)	The Ramones
The Hobbit (J.R.R. Tolkien)	David Bowie
The Grapes of Wrath (John Steinbeck)	Bruce Springsteen
Annabel Lee (Edgar Allen Poe)	Guns N' Roses
Pet Sematary (Stephen King)	The Velvet Underground
Catcher in the Rye (J.D. Salinger)	Stevie Nicks
Lolita (Vladimir Nabokov)	Lana Del Rey
1984 (George Orwell)	Iron Maiden
For Whom the Bell Tolls (Ernest Hemingway)	Leonard Nimoy
Brave New World (Aldous Huxley)	Metallica

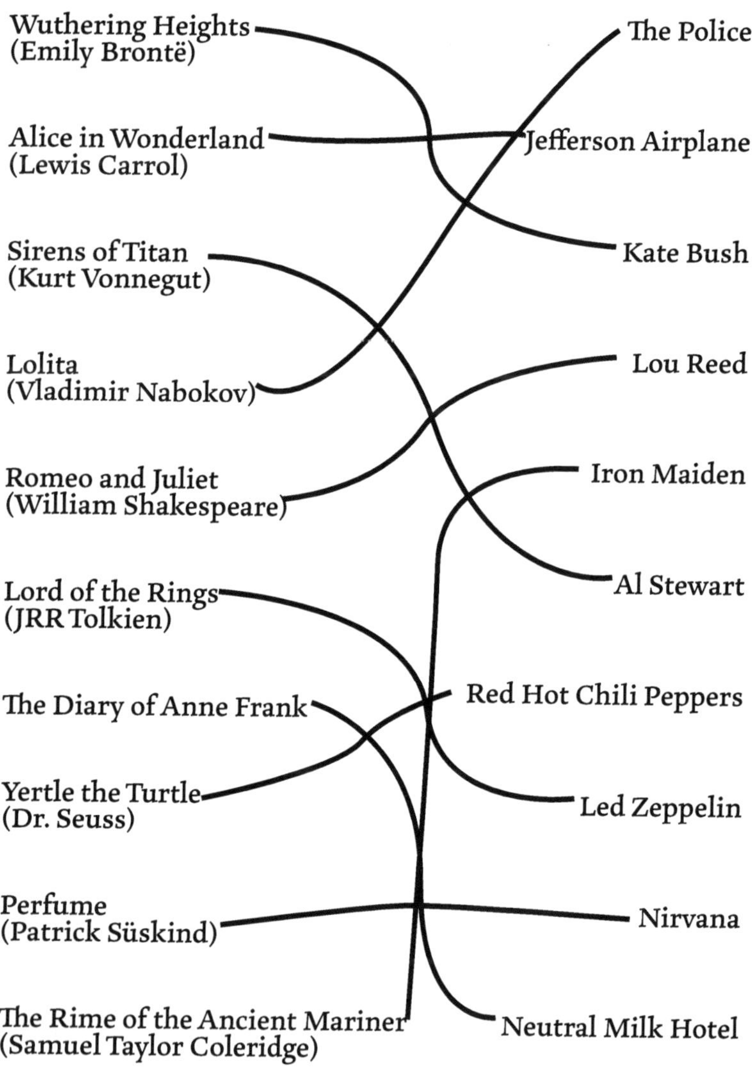
BOOKS
BANDS
Wuthering Heights
(Emily Brontë)
Alice in Wonderland
(Lewis Carrol)
Sirens of Titan
(Kurt Vonnegut)
Lolita
(Vladimir Nabokov)
Romeo and Juliet
(William Shakespeare)
Lord of the Rings
(JRR Tolkien)
The Diary of Anne Frank
Yertle the Turtle
(Dr. Seuss)
Perfume
(Patrick Süskind)
The Rime of the Ancient Mariner
(Samuel Taylor Coleridge)
The Police
Jefferson Airplane
Kate Bush
Lou Reed
Iron Maiden
Al Stewart
Red Hot Chili Peppers
Led Zeppelin
Nirvana
Neutral Milk Hotel

BOOKS

BANDS

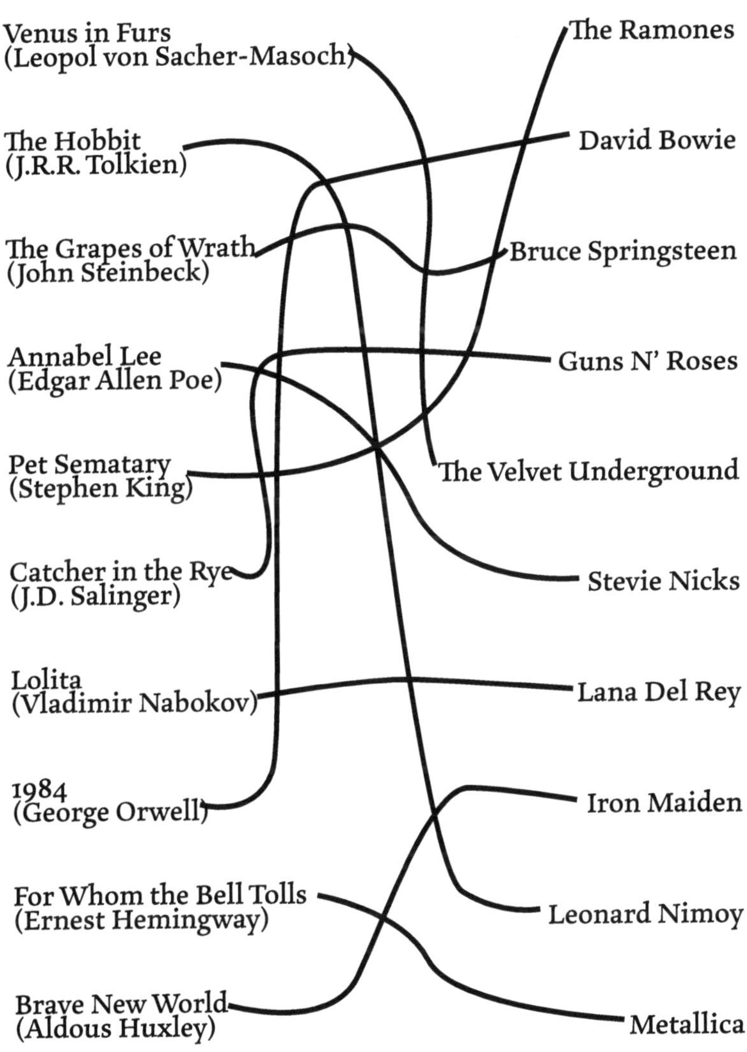
Venus in Furs
(Leopol von Sacher-Masoch)
The Hobbit
(J.R.R. Tolkien)
The Grapes of Wrath
(John Steinbeck)
Annabel Lee
(Edgar Allen Poe)
Pet Sematary
(Stephen King)
Catcher in the Rye
(J.D. Salinger)
Lolita
(Vladimir Nabokov)
1984
(George Orwell)
For Whom the Bell Tolls
(Ernest Hemingway)
Brave New World
(Aldous Huxley)
The Ramones
David Bowie
Bruce Springsteen
Guns N' Roses
The Velvet Underground
Stevie Nicks
Lana Del Rey
Iron Maiden
Leonard Nimoy
Metallica

SONGS TO BOOKS

Go to your local library and read some books. But you can do it while listening to some music:

Wuthering Heights (Emily Brontë): Kate Bush-*The Kick Inside*

Alice in Wonderland (Lewis Carrol): Jefferson Airplane-*Surrealistic Pillow*

Sirens of Titan (Kurt Vonnegut): Al Stewart-*Modern Times*

Lolita (Vladimir Nabokov): The Police-*Zenyatta Mondatta*

Lolita (Vladimir Nabokov): Lana Del Rey-*Born to Die*

Romeo and/Had Juliet/te (William Shakespeare): Lou Reed-*New York*

Lord of the Rings/Ramble On (JRR Tolkien): *Led Zeppelin II*

The Diary of Anne Frank: Neutral Milk Hotel-*In the Aeroplane Over the Sea*

Yertle the Turtle (Dr. Seuss): Red Hot Chili Peppers-*Freaky Styley*

Perfume/Scentless Apprentice (Patrick Süskind): Nirvana-*In Utero*

The Rime of the Ancient Mariner (Samuel Taylor Coleridge): Iron Maiden-*Powerslave*

Venus in Furs (Leopold von Sacher-Masoch)*: The Velvet Underground & Nico*

The Hobbit/The Ballad of Bilbo Baggins (J.R.R. Tolkien):
Leonard Nimoy- Watch the video on youtube.

The Grapes of Wrath (John Steinbeck): Bruce Springsteen-*The Ghost of Tom Joad*

Annabel Lee (Edgar Allen Poe): Stevie Nicks-*In Your Dreams*

Pet Sematary (Stephen King): The Ramones-*Brain Drain*

Catcher in the Rye (J.D. Salinger): Guns N' Roses-*Chinese Democracy*

1984 (George Orwell): David Bowie-*Diamond Dogs*

For Whom the Bell Tolls (Ernest Hemingway): Metallica-*Ride the Lightning, Live Shit*

Brave New World (Aldous Huxley): Iron Maiden-*Brave New World*

1. **On the Seinfeld episode, "The Checks," when Elaine's boyfriend is enraptured by "Desperado," which other Eagles' song does she try to make "theirs"?**
    a. Take It Easy
    b. Take It to the Limit
    c. Witchy Woman
    d. One of These Nights

2. **The 1971 Concerts for Bangladesh was the first time which artist played before paying customers since 1966?**
    a. Eric Clapton
    b. George Harrison
    c. Bob Dylan
    d. Donovan

3. **Who is the only artist to win the Mercury Prize for best British or Irish album twice?**
    a. U2
    b. The Beatles
    c. Oasis
    d. PJ Harvey

4. **What song had the longest journey to get to #1, debuting in 1994 and not reaching the top until Christmas in 2019 (although chances are that wasn't the first Christmas you heard it)?**

ANSWERS

1. **"Witchy Woman"**

   Eagle Bernie Leadon first started writing "Witchy Woman" when he was in The Flying Burrito Brothers with Gram Parsons.

   Recommended Album(s): *Eagles*

2. **George Harrison**

   Playing on rooftops doesn't count.

   Recommended Album(s): *The Concert for Bangladesh*

3. **PJ Harvey**

   She won them for 2000's *Stories from the City, Stories from the Sea* and 2011's *Let England Shake* and she totally deserved them.

   Recommended Album(s): Those two and *Rid of Me*

4. **Mariah Carey's "All I Want for Christmas is You"**

   It has sold over 17 million copies.

   Recommended Album(s): You don't have to buy it—just go to a mall in December. Or turn on the radio.

1. **Which classic rock bassist was known as "The Ox"?**
    a. John Paul Jones
    b. Bill Wyman
    c. Geddy Lee
    d. John Entwistle

2. **Which all-female band from Los Angeles recorded a minor hit in 1976 that ended up in the *Guardians of the Galaxy*?**
    a. The Go-Go's
    b. The Runaways
    c. The Germs
    d. The Avengers

3. **Who gave us the musical lesson that peaches come from a can?**
    a. Weezer
    b. The Presidents of the United States of America
    c. The Butthole Surfers
    d. Cake

4. **What is the best-selling album of all time with sales of over 66 million?**

ANSWERS

1. **John Entwistle**

   He started by playing jazz trumpet with Pete Townshend, before they decided rock 'n' roll was more fun. He tried guitar, but his fingers were too thick and so he took up bass. Then he played with Roger Daltrey for a bit, before they all formed The Who.

   Recommended Album(s): The Who's *Live at Leeds*

2. **The Runaways**

   The song was "Cherry Bomb." Joan Jett wrote it on the spot for eventual lead singer Cherie Currie's audition, since the band didn't know the song she had chosen.

   Recommended Album(s): *The Runaways*

3. **The Presidents of the United States of America**

   They were put there by a man. The "Peaches" single only hit #29, but in summer of 1996, you couldn't escape it.

   Recommended Album(s): *The Presidents of the United States of America*

4. **Michael Jackson's *Thriller***

   Thriller sold 33 million copies in its first year alone. That's more than Bob Dylan had sold period, by that point.

   Recommended Album(s): *Thriller*

INDIE ROCK VS ALTERNATIVE

Indie rock fans love to argue about what constitutes indie rock. Some of them also "dance" by swaying slightly, while avoiding eye contact with one another.

"Indie" was originally supposed to mean, well, independent. Not with the major labels, DIY and all that. So, not that useful a phrase, since your band might be emo, death metal, or jangle pop and still indie. So, the name evolved to basically mean a band that's starting to get some notice, but not enough that they're not cool anymore.

"Alternative" is even worse. Nirvana's Nevermind *is alternative, because it was an alternative to the mainstream, but then it became the mainstream. Camper Van Beethoven was indie and small, but then migrated to become Cracker and signed with Virgin to become alternative, but maybe they were just rock? In the 1980s, and into the 1990s, "college rock" covered a lot of these bands, but then college djs didn't know what to do when these bands hit it big.*

Is that helpful?

INDIE ROCK

1. **Which critics-darling band has been composed of Ira Kaplan, Georgia Hubley, and James McNew for the majority of its existence?**
    a. Times New Viking
    b. SF Seals
    c. Hypnolovewheel
    d. Yo La Tengo

2. **Whose magnum opus (so far) is *69 Love Songs*?**
    a. The Magnetic Fields
    b. The 6ths
    c. The Gothic Archies
    d. Future Bible Heroes

3. **Durham's Merge Records originally started as a way to release which band's records, fronted by Laura Ballance and Mac McCaughan?**
    a. Superchunk
    b. Neutral Milk Hotel
    c. Lambchop
    d. The Rosebuds

4. **What indie supergroup is composed of Zumpano's Carl Newman, Destroyer's Dan Bejar, vocal tornado Neko Case, and others?**

1. **Which 1992 hit, written by Linda Perry, had its title changed, so as not to confuse it with a Marvin Gaye song?**
    a. Come Out and Play
    b. What's Up?
    c. Save the Child
    d. What I Got

2. **Which of these bands has Jack White NOT been a member of?**
    a. The Black Keys
    b. The White Stripes
    c. The Dead Weather
    d. The Raconteurs

3. **Which woman holds the record for the most Grammy nominations for Best Alternative Album, tied at eight with Radiohead and Beck?**
    a. Fiona Apple
    b. Björk
    c. Tori Amos
    d. PJ Harvey

4. **What anarcho-communist punk-folk-dance band had a surprise hit (especially to themselves) in 1998 with "Tubthumping"?**

INDIE ROCK

1. **Yo La Tengo**

   A YLT show might feature a bevy of delicate strings, an hour of throbbing feedback, a surprise appearance from members of the Sun Ra Arkestra or Fred Armisen, or a re-enactment of a classic Simpsons episode.

   Recommended Album(s): *): I Can Hear the Heart Beating as One, I Am Not Afraid of You and I Will Beat Your Ass*

2. **The Magnetic Fields**

   Stephin Merritt (the leader of all four bands) has pointed out on numerous occasions that it is not an album about love, but rather about love songs.

   Recommended Album(s): *69 Love Songs*

3. **Superchunk**

   The label has since topped the charts and won Grammys with bands like Arcade Fire, Camera Obscura, Waxahatchee, and She & Him.

   Recommended Album(s): Arcade Fire's *The Suburbs,* Spoon's *Ga Ga Ga Ga,* and Superchunk's *No Pocky for Kitty*

4. **The New Pornographers**

   They're super, and they're a group of people from different bands, so the label fits. The pride of Vancouver, they've released eight albums, while keeping up their day bands.

   Recommended Album(s): *Mass Romantic, Electric Version*

1. **"What's Up?," not "What's Going On"**

   Perry didn't like the production on the single and their next album was more mainstream, which alienated some fans. But she started writing/producing songs for Christian Aguilera, Gwen Stefani, P!nk, Adele, and Alicia Keys, so hopefully she's happy now.

   Recommended Album(s): *Bigger, Better, Faster, More!*

2. **The Black Keys**

   After forming the White Stripes with his "sister" Meg, Jack has brought his blues/garage/etc. stylings to many bands, while running his Third Man Records label (and upholstering studio).

   Recommended Album(s): Can't go wrong, but how about the White Stripes' *Elephant.* Or hell, go check out Loretta Lynn's *Van Lear Rose,* which he produced.

3. **Björk**

   She's had 15 total Grammy nominations, but no wins to date.

   Recommended Album(s): *Post* or maybe *Homegenic*

4. **Chumbawamba**

   When Nike offered them $1.5 million to use the song, it took 30 seconds to say no. However, they did take $100,000 from GM for a Pontiac ad, which they gave to anti-corporate activist groups for an anti-GM campaign.

   Recommended Album(s): *Tubthumper*

WINNER: INDIE ROCK

Before you kids and your streaming came along, it was often hard to find new bands. Sometimes you'd be at In Your Ear in Boston or Moby Disc in LA, and would find a 45 or an lp with a cool cover and you'd flip it over and if you trusted the label, you might buy it. These are some of those labels:

Creation: *Britpop (Teenage Fanclub, Super Furry Animals, Primal Scream, Oasis)*

Sub Pop: *Grunge, Indie (Mudhoney, Nirvana, Soundgarden, Sleater-Kinney)*

4AD: *Alternative, Dream Pop, Goth (Bauhaus, Pixies, Throwing Muses, Belly)*

Matador: *Indie, Punk, Experimental (Yo La Tengo, Cat Power, Pizzicato Five, New Pornographers)*

Merge: *Indie, Alternative (Superchunk, Spoon, Magnetic Fields, Arcade Fire)*

Kill Rock Stars: *Indie, Punk, Riot Grrrl (Comet Gain, Bikini Kill, The Thermals, Bratmobile, Mary Lou Lord)*

1. **Which shock rocker played the part of Herod in the 2018 live NBC version of *Jesus Christ Superstar*?**
    a. Screaming Lord Sutch
    b. Marilyn Manson
    c. Screaming Jay Hawkins
    d. Alice Cooper

2. **Who had a #4 single with "Groove is in the Heart" in 1990?**
    a. Jungle Brothers
    b. A Tribe Called Quest
    c. Deee-Lite
    d. De La Soul

3. **Who is the only member of the Cure to be in every lineup?**
    a. Robert Smith
    b. Mick Dempsey
    c. Lol Tolhurst
    d. Alan Hill

4. **What Rolling Stones song was written about David Bowie's wife at the time?**

ANSWERS

1. **Alice Cooper**

   John Legend played Jesus and Sara Bareilles was Mary Magdalene, but Cooper stole the show.

   Recommended Album(s): While this version was fun, the 2012 UK Arena Tour version with Tim Minchin as Judas Iscariot and Melanie C (aka Sporty Spice) as Mary Magdalene is the one you want to check out.

2. **Deee-Lite**

   An instant hit in nightclubs in the US and Europe, it featured Parliament's Bootsy Collins and Q-Tip from A Tribe Called Quest.

   Recommended Album(s): *World Clique*

3. **Robert Smith**

   The other three all played together in middle school. I'm guessing it was a bit of a moody middle school.

   Recommended Album(s): *Pornography* (gloomy) or *Disintegration* (less gloomy)

4. **"Angie"**

   Angela Bowie talked at length about barging in on Mick and David in bed together. Others will use "facts" to say that Keith wrote most of the song and that it's about his daughter Angie. But shouldn't a good story be better than all those dreams that go up in smoke?

   Recommended Album(s): *Goat's Head Soup*

US #1 SINGLES

These ten artists have more US #1 singles than anyone else. Can you rank them in order correctly? Can you guess how many each had?

Rank		*Number*
_____	*Whitney Houston*	_____
_____	*Elvis Presley*	_____
_____	*Mariah Carey*	_____
_____	*Michael Jackson*	_____
_____	*Janet Jackson*	_____
_____	*The Beatles*	_____
_____	*Rihanna*	_____
_____	*Madonna*	_____
_____	*Stevie Wonder*	_____
_____	*The Supremes*	_____

US #1 SINGLES

Rank		Number
8	*Whitney Houston*	11
3	*Elvis Presley*	18
2	*Mariah Carey*	19
5	*Michael Jackson*	13
9	*Janet Jackson*	10
1	*The Beatles*	20
4	*Rihanna*	14
6	*Madonna*	12
9	*Stevie Wonder*	10
6	*The Supremes*	12

1. **Which rock opera involved a boy interpreting various senses into music?**
    a. *Arthur (Or the Decline and Fall of the British Empire)*
    b. *Tommy*
    c. *Ziggy Stardust*
    d. *Aqualung*

2. **Which rapper, who died in 2021 at the age of 50, was the first artist to have their first five albums reach #1?**
    a. Mike Adam Yauch
    b. Nipsey Hussle
    c. Pop Smoke
    d. DMX

3. **Which band was formed after the singer posted an advertisement looking for a bass player who liked Peter, Paul and Mary, as well as Hüsker Dü?**
    a. The Pixies
    b. Nirvana
    c. The Lemonheads
    d. Yo La Tengo

4. **What song did Stevie Wonder write in tribute to Duke Ellington, after he died in 1974?**

ANSWERS

1. **The Who's *Tommy***

   After they recorded it, they would play it fully in concerts, then there was an orchestra version in 1972 (with Steve Winwood, Rod Stewart, Ringo Starr, Richie Havens, Sandy Denny, and Merry Clayton), a movie in 1975, and a Broadway show in 1992.

   Recommended Album(s): *Tommy*

2. **DMX**

   Starting off as a beatboxer, his debut, *It's Dark and Hell is Hot* sold 251,000 copies in its first week.

   Recommended Album(s): *...And Then There Was X*

3. **The Pixies**

   Kim Deal soon joined and tried to get her sister Kelley on drums, but she didn't feel ready and recommended David Lovering to join Black Francis and Joey Santiago. Kelly later joined Kim in the Breeders.

   Recommended Album(s): *Surfer Rosa, Doolittle*

4. **"Sir Duke"**

   He didn't want Duke to be forgotten, or the other musicians he mentions, like Sodarisa Miller, Louis Armstrong, Count Basie, and Ella Fitzgerald.

   Recommended Album(s): *Songs in the Key of Life*

1. **David Sanborn and Luther Vandross played on which classic David Bowie album?**
   a. *Low*
   b. *Young Americans*
   c. *Aladdin Sane*
   d. *Station to Station*

2. **Which song, which they wrote together, appeared on Iggy Pop's 1977 *The Idiot* lp and David Bowie's 1983 *Let's Dance*?**
   a. China Girl
   b. Modern Love
   c. Sister Midnight
   d. Let's Dance

3. **What did David Bowie call the kids who waited outside the Philadelphia studio everyday while he recorded *Young Americans*?**
   a. Philly Scum
   b. The Sigma Kids
   c. The Sweathogs
   d. Gritty

4. **On what tv show did David Bowie play "TVC-15," "Man Who Sold the World," and "Boys Keep Swinging" in 1979?**

ANSWERS

1. ***Young Americans***

   Sanborn played a sax with a wah-wah pedal, which sounds pretty cool. And Luther Vandross sang backup on the 1975 lp.

   Recommended Album(s): *Young Americans*

2. **"China Girl"**

   It was the first song they wrote when they tried to escape the drug scene in Los Angeles. Nile Rodgers, the producer of the later version, thought it was about speedballing.

   Recommended Album(s): *The Idiot, Let's Dance*

3. **The Sigma Kids**

   On his final day in the studio, he brought them all inside to hear the rough mix.

   Recommended Album(s): *Young Americans*

4. **Saturday Night Live**

   He had artists Klaus Nomi and Joey Arias carry him out in a plastic tuxedo. There were also small dogs with televisions in their mouths. It was genius.

   Recommended Album(s): I gotta say everything, but get *Never Let Me Down* last.

1. **What was Joni Mitchell's first gold record album (more than half a million in sales)?**
    a. *Blue*
    b. *Hejira*
    c. *Ladies of the Canyon*
    d. *Court and Spark*

2. **Which song off *Hejira* did Joni Mitchell write about playwright Sam Shepherd, probably while on Bob Dylan's Rolling Thunder Revue tour?**
    a. Coyote
    b. Amelia
    c. Furry Sings the Blues
    d. Refuge of the Roads

3. **Joni Mitchell's "The Circle Game" is a response to which Neil Young song?**
    a. Sugar Mountain
    b. Down by the River
    c. Harvest
    d. Cinnamon Girl

4. **For her debut album, *Song to a Seagull,* who was the producer who thought it would be good idea for Joni to sing into a grand piano to capture her voice reverberating off the strings? It's possible he was high at the time.**

ANSWERS

1. ***Ladies of the Canyon***

   "Big Yellow Taxi" was probably enough to make it go gold, but it also had "Circle Game," "For Free," and "Woodstock."

   Recommended Album(s): *Ladies of the Canyon*

2. **"Coyote"**

   "Now he's got a woman at home / He's got another woman down the hall / He seems to want me anyway."

   Recommended Album(s): *Hejira*

3. **"Sugar Mountain"**

   Neil wrote it about his disappointment at aging out of his favorite teeny bopper club, so Joni wrote hers to give him some hope.

   Recommended Album(s): Joni Mitchell's *Ladies of the Canyon,* Neil Young's *Decade* compilation, but maybe not on Spotify

4. **David Crosby**

   It was a not a good idea.

   Recommended Album(s): Still some good songs on the album, but you'll like *Clouds* better than that, and then *Ladies of the Canyon* came out, and then OMIGOD *Blue*, and so on. 2022 UPDATE: Songs to a Seagull has been remastered and is much improved. Maybe it was just my worn-down vinyl copy.

1. **Who was Lynyrd Skynyrd named after?**
   a. A confederate general
   b. A Jacksonville PE teacher
   c. A local Jacksonville weed dealer
   d. A recurring character on the tv show, *Mod Squad*

2. **Lowell George supposedly formed Little Feat after being asked to leave what band for writing a song about dope ("Willin")?**
   a. Frank Zappa's Mothers of Invention
   b. The Chad Mitchell Trio
   c. The Association
   d. The Hollies

3. **Which of the following places is it *possible*, although unlikely, that Right Said Fred is not too sexy for?**
   a. New York
   b. Japan
   c. London
   d. Milan

4. **Whose debut album in 1995, *Relish*, led to nominations for Album of the Year, Record of the Year, and Song of the Year?**

ANSWERS

1. **A Jacksonville PE teacher**

   The band met in school in the mid-sixties and released their first album in 1973. A plane crash killed Ronnie Van Zant, Steve Gaines, and Chrissie Gaines, but they reformed ten years later with Ronnie's brother, Johnny.

   Recommended Album(s): *Pronounced 'Lêh-'nérd 'Skin-'nérd)* and *One More From the Road*

2. **Frank Zappa's Mothers of Invention**

   In college, when a woman at a party told me she liked Little Feat, I asked her to name me three songs. I meant this to be a knock at Little Feat, but of course it was a rude insult to her and inexcusable. I don't think I can even chalk it up to bad flirting. I would sincerely like to apologize to her and to Little Feat.

   Recommended Album(s): *Sailin' Shoes*

3. **London**

   The two Fairbrass brothers who made up Right Said Fred had more international hits, but not so much in the US.

   Recommended Album(s): *Up*

4. **Joan Osborne**

   The big song, "One of Us," starts off with a field recording Alan Lomax made in 1937.

   Recommended Album(s): *Relish*

BOB DYLAN COVERS

Match the tune with the artist who famously covered it.

Blowin' in the Wind	Rage Against the Machine
The Mighty Quinn	Peter, Paul & Mary
Knockin' on Heaven's Door	Eric Clapton
All Along the Watchtower	The Byrds
Mr. Tambourine Man	Guns N' Roses
Maggie's Farm	Adele
Make You Feel My Love	Garth Brooks
It Ain't Me, Babe	Billy Joel
Highway 61 Revisited	Jimi Hendrix
If Not for You	Manfred Mann
	George Harrison
	PJ Harvey
	June & Johnny Cash

BOB DYLAN COVERS

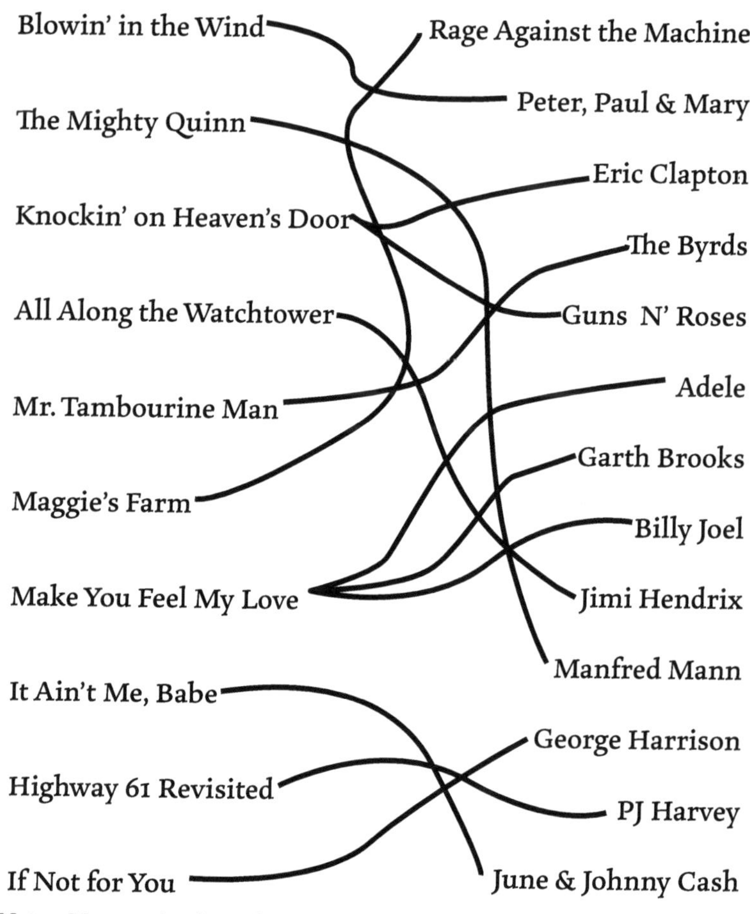

Notes: Many artists have done whole albums of his songs – that's why Graham Nash left the Hollies. Billy Joel had the first release of 1997's "Make You Feel My Love" (before Dylan's), Garth Brooks took it to the top of the country charts, but more people now probably know Adele's version, because, well, she's Adele. Now, if Chris Gaines had done it...

Recommended Albums: Dylan fans argue endlessly about the cover versions, but they all agree you should buy Hendrix's *Electric Ladyland.*

QUESTIONS

1. **The outfits in which early MTV video provided the fashion guidance for Sonny Crockett (Don Johnson) in Miami Vice?**
    a. Hungry Like the Wolf
    b. You Got Lucky
    c. Love Is a Battlefield
    d. Billy Jean

2. **Who wrote and produced Mott the Hoople's biggest hit?**
    a. David Bowie
    b. Iggy Pop
    c. Ian Hunter
    d. Al Kooper

3. **Who is the only artist to have a single bumped out of #1 on the charts by themselves twice over three weeks?**
    a. The Beatles
    b. The Bee Gees
    c. Fleetwood Mac
    d. Beyoncé

4. **Which band had the first US #1 sung mostly in Korean, in 2020?**

ANSWERS

1. **"Hungry Like the Wolf"**

   It's like MTV was designed for Duran Duran.

   Recommended Album(s): *Rio*

2. **David Bowie**

   Bowie made a demo of "Suffragette City" and sent it to them in February 1972. They tried it, decided it didn't fit their sound and then told Bowie they were breaking up. He called them two hours later and said he wrote a new song for them and don't break up. He came by a couple days later and played "All the Young Dudes" for them on his acoustic guitar.

   Recommended Album(s): *All the Young Dudes*

3. **The Beatles**

   Over three weeks in 1964, the top spot went from "I Want to Hold Your Hand" to "She Loves You" to "Can't Buy Me Love."

   Recommended Album(s): *Meet the Beatles!*

4. **BTS**

   Do not get BTS fans angry. Let me be absolutely clear that I love BTS and am willing to pledge my allegiance to them.

   Recommended Album(s): Everything! Buy them all! Please don't hurt me.

COPYRIGHT BATTLES

December 5th, 1704, George Frideric Handel (as in the Messiah Hallelujah Chorus—not the Leonard Cohen/ John Cale/Shrek/Jeff Buckley/etc. one) got into a fight with Johann Mattheson about who should be conducting. Mid-performance they left the opera hall and dueled outside, a large metal button the only thing saving Handel from a fatal sword thrust. OG.

And this was before Handel started stealing Mattheson's melodies. And then Mozart start ripping off Haydn and on and on. Hell, Homer was probably pissed that he wasn't getting royalties every time some two-bit fireside poet started chanting the Iliad. *But ancient Greek Spotify would probably only pay 0.0001 drachma per stream anyhow.*

The earliest American legal case was in 1844 (against that infamous magazine, The Ladies Companion*), but court cases didn't start taking off until the late 20th Century, when the money made it worth it. Sadly, many cases (often not making it to court) involved white artists taking melodies and more from Black blues or R&B musicians.*

Much of the time, the plagiarism is unintentional, and the offending artist realizes it and settles out of court. But sometimes they fight tooth and nail. On the next two pages, match the famous song with the song it (allegedly) took from and the original artist.

THE ACCUSED	ORIGINAL SONG
Surfin' USA (The Beach Boys)	The Air That I Breathe
Stairway to Heaven (Led Zeppelin)	Sweet Little Sixteen
My Sweet Lord (George Harrison)	Under Pressure
Hello, I Love You (The Doors)	The Last Time
Creep (Radiohead)	Taurus
Ice Ice Baby (Vanilla Ice)	He's So Fine
Letter B (Sesame Street)	Run Through the Jungle
Bittersweet Symphony (The Verve)	You Really Got Me
The Old Man Down the Road (John Fogerty)	Got to Give It Up
Blurred Lines (Robin Thicke & Pharrell Williams)	Let It Be

ORIGINAL SONG

The Air That I Breathe

Sweet Little Sixteen

Under Pressure

The Last Time

Taurus

He's So Fine

Run Through the Jungle

You Really Got Me

Got to Give It Up

Let It Be

THE ACCUSER

Queen & David Bowie

The Rolling Stones

Chuck Berry

Spirit

The Hollies (Albert Hammond)

The Kinks

The Beatles

Marvin Gaye

The Chiffons (Ronnie Mack)

Creedence Clearwater Revival

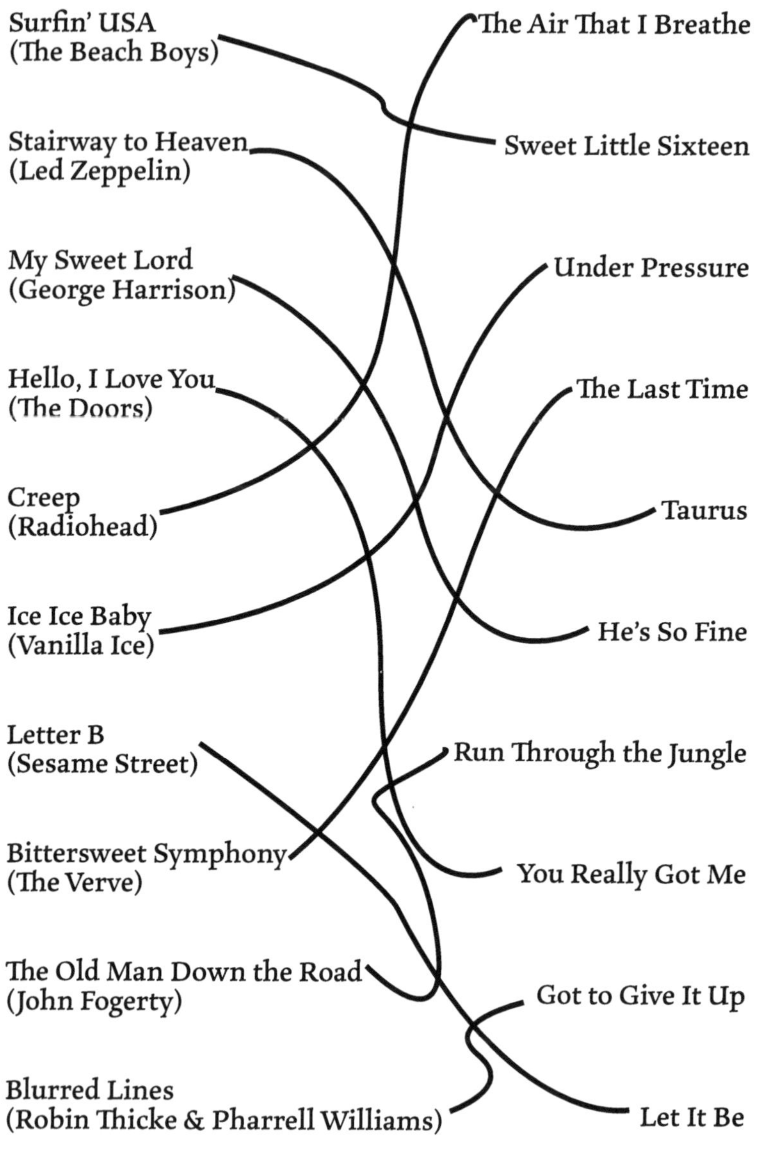
THE ACCUSED
ORIGINAL SONG
Surfin' USA
(The Beach Boys)
The Air That I Breathe
Stairway to Heaven
(Led Zeppelin)
Sweet Little Sixteen
My Sweet Lord
(George Harrison)
Under Pressure
Hello, I Love You
(The Doors)
The Last Time
Creep
(Radiohead)
Taurus
Ice Ice Baby
(Vanilla Ice)
He's So Fine
Letter B
(Sesame Street)
Run Through the Jungle
Bittersweet Symphony
(The Verve)
You Really Got Me
The Old Man Down the Road
(John Fogerty)
Got to Give It Up
Blurred Lines
(Robin Thicke & Pharrell Williams)
Let It Be

ORIGINAL SONG
THE ACCUSER
The Air That I Breathe
Queen & David Bowie
Sweet Little Sixteen
The Rolling Stones
Under Pressure
Chuck Berry
The Last Time
Spirit
Taurus
The Hollies (Albert Hammond)
He's So Fine
The Kinks
Run Through the Jungle
The Beatles
You Really Got Me
Marvin Gaye
Got to Give It Up
The Chiffons (Ronnie Mack)
Let It Be
Creedence Clearwater Revival

COPYRIGHT BATTLES

Surfin' USA: Chuck Berry soon got both credit and royalties. Chuck Berry: *The Definitive Collection;* The Beach Boys: *Surfin' USA*

Stairway to Heaven: Go listen to "Taurus" by Spirit. Hmm? But the court sided with Led Zeppelin, saying it needed to be "virtually identical." Spirit: *Spirit;* Led Zeppelin: *IV*

My Sweet Lord: George Harrison said he was surprised he hadn't realized the similarity and he ended up sharing royalties. The Chiffons: *He's So Fine;* George Harrison: *All Things Must Pass*

Hello, I Love You: Kink Ray Davies was satisfied once The Doors admitted to it. The Kinks: *Kinks-Size;* The Doors: *Waiting for the Sun*

Creep: They came to an undisclosed agreement. Later, Radiohead sued Lana Del Rey, for infringing on "Creep." It's like an onion. Layers. Albert Hammond: *It Never Rains in Southern California;* The Hollies: *Hollies;* Radiohead: *Pablo Honey*

Ice Ice Baby: I can remember being underage in a funky bar in 1989 when the added note came on & we all stopped and looked at each other. Queen & David Bowie: Everything

Letter B: The Beatles themselves liked the tribute, but their publishing house didn't. Luckily, Michael Jackson went and bought the entire catalog and stopped the suit. The Beatles: *Let It Be;* Sesame Street: just support Sesame Street.

Bittersweet Symphony: The Verve had sampled a six-second bit but didn't get permission from all the copyright holders. The Rolling Stones: *Out of Our Heads;* The Verve: *Urban Hymns*

The Old Man Down the Road: He got sued for sounding like himself. Creedence Clearwater Revival: *Cosmo's Factory;* John Fogerty: *Centerfield*

Blurred Lines: Let me stay this up front: do not talk to women this way. Or men. In terms of plagiarism, it was a landmark case because the decision rested on the feel of the song. Marvin Gaye: *Live at the London Palladium;* Robin Thicke & Pharrell Williams: *Blurred Lines*

1. **Which album was Brian Wilson speaking of when he told friends at dinner that he was making a "teenage symphony to God"?**
   a. *Smile*
   b. *Pet Sounds*
   c. *Wild Honey*
   d. *Endless Summer*

2. **Who briefly worked for his father's accounting firm in 1970 after he left his first band?**
   a. Stephen Stills
   b. Jeff Beck
   c. Lou Reed
   d. Frank Zappa

3. **Who began a string of five consecutive #1 singles with 2010's "California Gurls"?**
   a. Katy Perry
   b. Snoop Dogg
   c. Lady Gaga
   d. Beyoncé

4. **According to a 1980 movie comedy, what two types of music do they play at Bob's Country Bunker, south of Chicago?**

ANSWERS

1. ***Smile***

   The Beach Boys weren't able to finish this follow-up to *Pet Sounds* at the time. Songs and pieces ended up on various albums, bootlegs proliferated, Brian Wilson released a solo version in 2004, and finally in 2011 it was released, along with hours and hours from the session.

   Recommended Album(s): *The Smile Sessions*

2. **Lou Reed**

   Was he the coolest accountant in New York? Didn't Paul Simon write a song about that?

   Recommended Album(s): His eponymous lp was his next one, but then he made *Transformer*, and could probably start paying for an accountant.

3. **Katy Perry**

   Snoop Dogg co-wrote "California Gurls" with her and others and sang on it.

   Recommended Album(s): *Teenage Dream*

4. **Both kinds, Country *and* Western**

   The Blues Brothers can learn "Wreck of the Old '97" for next time.

   Recommended Album(s): *The Blues Brothers: Original Soundtrack Recording*

1. **Who introduced marijuana to the Beatles?**
   a. Keith Richards
   b. David Crosby
   c. Donovan
   d. Bob Dylan

2. **Which Bob Marley song did Joe Strummer of the Clash and Johnny Cash record together?**
   a. Redemption Song
   b. Three Little Birds
   c. No Woman No Cry
   d. Buffalo Soldier

3. **Which of the following did not sing on the 2001 *Moulin Rouge!* version of Labelle's "Lady Marmalade"?**
   a. Christina Aguilera
   b. Missy Elliot
   c. Lil' Kim
   d. Pink
   e. Mya

4. **What band's early hits primarily featured one brother singing and later hits featured another, to the tune of over 200 million albums?**

ANSWERS

1. **Bob Dylan**

   Dylan was surprised, since he thought they sang "I get high" in "I Want to Hold Your Hand." They put down towels at the bottom of hotel room doors, just in case. And six years later they broke up—so let that be a lesson to you.

   Recommended Album(s): *The Beatles* (The White Album)

2. **"Redemption Song"**

   Strummer spent ten days lying on the floor of Cash's studio, watching him record, before building up the nerve to sing with him.

   Recommended Album(s): You can find it on Cash's 5-cd *Unearthed* boxset.

3. **Missy Elliott**

   Missy Elliott produced it, but did not sing on the single, which spent five weeks at #1, 26 years after the original also hit #1. Baz Lurhman supposedly wanted some K-pop stars on it too, but no such luck.

   Recommended Album(s): *Moulin Rouge! Soundtrack*

4. **The Bee Gees**

   Robin Gibb and his clear vibrato was the early lead, switching to Barry Gibb's falsetto as disco became king.

   Recommended Album(s): *Children of the World*

CBGB VS. THE FILLMORE

The original Fillmore opened in San Francisco in 1912, as the Majestic Hall. It held concerts and dances (and was a roller-skating rink in the 1940s) and Bill Graham started booking there in 1965. It became the poster child of the Love-In Sixties (or at least, had the best posters).

Opening in 1973, famed NYC club CBGB had two rules for its bands—play (mostly) originals and move your own damn equipment. It became the epicenter for punk and new wave.

CBGB

1. **One of the first songs Debbie Harry and Chris Stein of Blondie wrote was called "The Disco Song," until they came up with what title while recording?**
    a. Call Me
    b. The Tide Is High
    c. Atomic
    d. Heart of Glass

2. **Which Ramones' tune did they write when Joey ended up in the hospital after burning himself?**
    a. Blitzkrieg Bop
    b. I Wanna Be Sedated
    c. Now I Wanna Sniff Some Glue
    d. Gimme Gimme Shock Treatment

3. **Who closed out CBGB on October 15, 2006?**
    a. The Talking Heads
    b. Patti Smith
    c. Television
    d. Green Day

4. **What did CBGB stand for? Or give the full name, CBGB & OMFUG, for extra credit.**

THE FILLMORE

1. **What was the first act that Bill Graham booked at the Fillmore?**
    a. San Francisco Mime Troupe
    b. The Grateful Dead
    c. Jefferson Airplane
    d. Fred Neil

2. **When did Bill Graham move the Fillmore a mile and a half and rename it Fillmore West?**
    a. 1966
    b. 1968
    c. 1972
    d. 1984

3. **What was the Fillmore called in the 1980s when it was punk venue?**
    a. The Troubador
    b. Bottom of the Hill
    c. The Elite Club
    d. 924 Gilman Street

4. **What was the name of Jefferson Airplane's first live lp, which they recorded at the Fillmores, West & East?**

CBGB

1. **"Heart of Glass"**

   Being in the CBGB's environment of NYC, they wanted to do some disco to be different from the underground. They also found many US radio stations were censoring their "pain in the ass" line.

   Recommended Album(s): *Parallel Lines*

2. **"I Wanna Be Sedated"**

   The chorus about nothing to do comes from being in London at Christmas, with everything closed. And, yes, Joey Ramone's guitar solo is the same note, 65 times in a row.

   Recommended Album(s): *Road to Ruin*

3. **Patti Smith**

   Rising rents finally drove them out. She encored with "Elegie," naming all the CBGB artists who had died since it opened.

   Recommended Album(s): *Horses*

4. **Country, BlueGrass, and Blues & Other Music for Uplifting Gormandizers**

   Soon enough those styles had to take a backseat as the Ramones, Television, Patti Smith, Mink DeVille, Talking Heads, Blondie, The Damned, and others took over.

   Recommended Album(s): Hit all those artists, but also find a CBGB compilation or playlist to hear the bands that didn't last so long.

THE FILLMORE

1. **San Francisco Mime Troupe**

   This being San Francisco, it's one of those mime troupes that talks occasionally, incorporates jazz, and has had various run-ins with the police.

   Recommended Album(s): Not enough mimes do records, it's a shame.

2. **1968**

   He wanted a bigger place in a better neighborhood. The old place operated as the New Old Fillmore for a while.

   Recommended Album(s): *The Live Adventures of Mike Bloomfield and Al Kooper*

3. **The Elite Club**

   In the 1990s it was retrofitted and reopened as the Fillmore.

   Recommended Album(s): Go listen to some Social Distortion

4. ***Bless Its Pointed Little Head***

   Of the ten tunes, five were new and the old ones had more room to spread out.

   Recommended Album(s): *Bless Its Pointed Little Head*

WINNER: CBGB

The Fillmore had more bands, and bigger bands of diverse styles. But if there was no Fillmore, Bill Graham would have found some other place that would have worked as well. Everything had to go right and wrong for CBGB to exist.

1. **Which 1994 Rembrandts' song do some of your friends probably know really well, even though they don't know that we know that they know we know?**
    a. Welcome Back
    b. Everywhere You Look
    c. In the Street
    d. I'll Be There for You

2. **Which classic rock band included a member with a PhD in astrophysics?**
    a. The Grateful Dead
    b. Queen
    c. Jethro Tull
    d. Aerosmith

3. **What is eight for?**
    a. For my family
    b. For my headaches
    c. For my sorrow
    d. For no tomorrow
    e. I forget what eight was for

4. **What artist had her only #1 single six months after her death in October 1970?**

ANSWERS

1. **"I'll Be There for You"**

   The Rembrandts originally wrote just the one-minute theme song for the sitcom, *Friends*, but then a Nashville radio station looped it three times and suddenly the label wanted a single. It went to #17. And #1 on the Adult Contemporary chart, which, yeah, makes sense.

   Recommended Album(s): *L.P.*

2. **Queen**

   Once Queen hit it big, Brian May put his dissertation to the side, finally finishing it in 2007. It helped him write songs like "'39," dealing with the intricacies of time-space dilation.

   Recommended Album(s): *A Night at the Opera*

3. **I forget what eight was for**

   If you weren't around in the 1980s *and* cool, it's from "Kiss Off" by the Violent Femmes. In 1981, the Violent Femmes were busking in Milwaukee and the Pretenders saw them and had them come and play a set before them that night.

   Recommended Album(s): *Violent Femmes*

4. **Janis Joplin**

   The Kris Kristofferson-penned tune, "Me and Bobby McGee," became her most well-known song.

   Recommended Album(s): *Pearl*

SCRAMBLED ALBUMS

Can you decode the classic albums below?

Godfather Hustler

You can picture this folk rocker hanging out in his Topanga Canyon studio, like the original godfather hustler.

Northeast Femme

Born in NYC, so it's geographically correct. Her singing chops took her all the way to the inauguration in 2021.

Pandora Struck!

On this 1974 masterpiece, the artist spent some time dissecting the evils Pandora released.

Deworming Vuk Pungently

This 1994 lp debuted at #1, tragically after the lead singer died of suicide.

SCRAMBLED ALBUMS

Godfather Hustler
After the Goldrush

Neil Young: 1970
For years, boomers would struggle to get their joints out as soon as they heard the opening chords. Now it's their phones.

Northeast Femme
The Fame Monster

Lady Gaga: 2008/9
It's a combo reissue/new album, but the best anagram of *The Fame* is Math Fee, and no one wants that.

Pandora Struck!
Court and Spark

Joni Mitchell: 1974
It was at #2 for 4 weeks, kept out by Bob Dylan, Barbra Streisand, and John Denver.

Deworming Vuk Pungently
MTV Unplugged in New York

Nirvana: 1994
Besides their songs, they also covered David Bowie, bluesman Leadbelly, and the Meat Puppets (who played with them).

1. **What foundational LA punk band featured John Doe, Exene Cervenka, Billy Zoom, and D.J. Bonebrake?**
    a. W
    b. X
    c. Y
    d. Z

2. **Which member of Traffic wrote "Feelin' Alright?," later a hit for Joe Cocker?**
    a. Dave Mason
    b. Steve Winwood
    c. Jim Capaldi
    d. Chris Wood

3. **How old was Isaac Hanson (the eldest) when "MMMBop" when to #1 in 1997?**
    a. 11
    b. 13
    c. 16
    d. 19

4. **What soundtrack album produced a total of four #1 singles for two different artists in 1977?**

ANSWERS

1. **X**

   They had punk and they had rockabilly. They even had the Door's Ray Manzarek producing them.

   Recommended Album(s): *Los Angeles, Wild Gift,* and go check out the Knitters.

2. **Dave Mason**

   The Jackson 5 also did the song, but Joe Cocker had the biggest hit with it.

   Recommended Album(s): *Traffic,* Dave Mason's *Alone Together*

3. **16**

   The album sold over 10 million units and millions of Hanson fans still celebrate May 6 as Hanson Day. Or thousands of fans, anyways.

   Recommended Album(s): *Middle of Nowhere*

4. ***Saturday Night Fever***

   The Bee Gees had "How Deep Is Your Love," "Stayin' Alive," and "Night Fever," while Yvonne Elliman had "If I Can't Have You." It's probably Elliman that you forgot.

   Recommended Album(s): *Saturday Night Fever*

1. **Who was the first group of "hippie longhairs" to perform at Nashville's Grand Ole Opry, in 1968?**
    a. The Byrds
    b. Jefferson Airplane
    c. Hot Tuna
    d. The Grateful Dead

2. **Which artist recorded "Jump Around" after Cypress Hill and Ice Cube turned it down?**
    a. House of Pain
    b. Deee-Lite
    c. Salt 'n' Pepa
    d. Right Said Fred

3. **Which Tom Petty song did he and Bob Dylan write by pulling names out of a newspaper?**
    a. Breakdown
    b. Jammin' Me
    c. Louisiana Rain
    d. Mary Jane's Last Dance

4. **What Michael Jackson album had the most #1 singles of all time (five, now tied with Katy Perry's *Teenage Dream*)?**

ANSWERS

1. **The Byrds**

   Gram Parsons had joined the group and pushed them into a country-rock direction. They played Merle Haggard's "Sing Me Back Home" and Parson's "Hickory Wind."

   Recommended Album(s): *Sweetheart of the Rodeo*

2. **House of Pain**

   Cypress Hill did it later. Its horn section comes from Bob & Earl's original 1963 "Harlem Shuffle."

   Recommended Album(s): *House of Pain*

3. **"Jammin' Me"**

   Eddie Murphy, Vanessa Redgrave, Joe Piscopo, and Steve Jobs all got called out. But I guess Steve Jobs won, because who even knows what a newspaper is anymore?

   Recommended Album(s): *Let Me Up (I've Had Enough)*

4. ***Bad***

   You thought it was *Thriller*, didn't you? I did.

   Recommended Album(s): *Bad*

1. **Which Audrey Hepburn film did Deep Blue Something write their only hit about?**
    a. The Lavender Hill Mob
    b. Breakfast at Tiffany's
    c. Roman Holiday
    d. My Fair Lady

2. **Who did vocals on Jeff Beck's debut album, *Truth*?**
    a. Paul Rodgers
    b. Donovan
    c. Robert Plant
    d. Rod Stewart

3. **What was the name of the band with most of R.E.M. backing up Warren Zevon, who covered Prince's "Raspberry Beret" on their sole album, in 1990?**
    a. The Firm
    b. Hindu Love Gods
    c. Trawling for Olives
    d. The Werewolves of Atlanta

4. **What was the first video played on MTV?**

ANSWERS

1. ***Breakfast at Tiffany's***

   Ok, technically they wrote it about *Roman Holiday*, but "Breakfast at Tiffany's" fit the meter better. There are now couples breaking up where the only thing they have in common is that they both kind of liked the song.

   Recommended Album(s): *Home*

2. **Rod Stewart**

   This lp has been called a harbinger of heavy metal, but may have just been portending heavy blues.

   Recommended Album(s): *Truth*

3. **The Hindu Love Gods**

   An on-again, off-again somewhat-thrown together band, the album also included blues classics and the Georgia Satellites' "Battleship Chains."

   Recommended Album(s): *Hindu Love Gods*

4. **"Video Killed the Radio Star" by The Buggles**

   It was the Buggles' only hit. They recorded it 1979, two years before MTV launched. In the meantime, they had joined the group Yes and then left it again.

   Recommended Album(s): *English Garden,* or really, just find a new wave collection.

MUSIC FESTIVALS

Some say the Woodstock Nation started at Woodstock in August of 1969 and ended a few months later with the disaster at Altamont. Match up who was at which (or both).

WOODSTOCK

Melanie
Blood, Sweat & Tears
Santana
The Band
Joe Cocker
Arlo Guthrie
Creedence Clearwater Revival
Richie Havens
Johnny Winter
Jefferson Airplane
Country Joe McDonald
The Rolling Stones
Country Joe & the Fish
Sly and the Family Stone
The Flying Burrito Brothers
Joan Baez
The Who
The Grateful Dead
Jimi Hendrix
Janis Joplin
Crosby, Stills, Nash & Young

ALTAMONT

MUSIC FESTIVALS

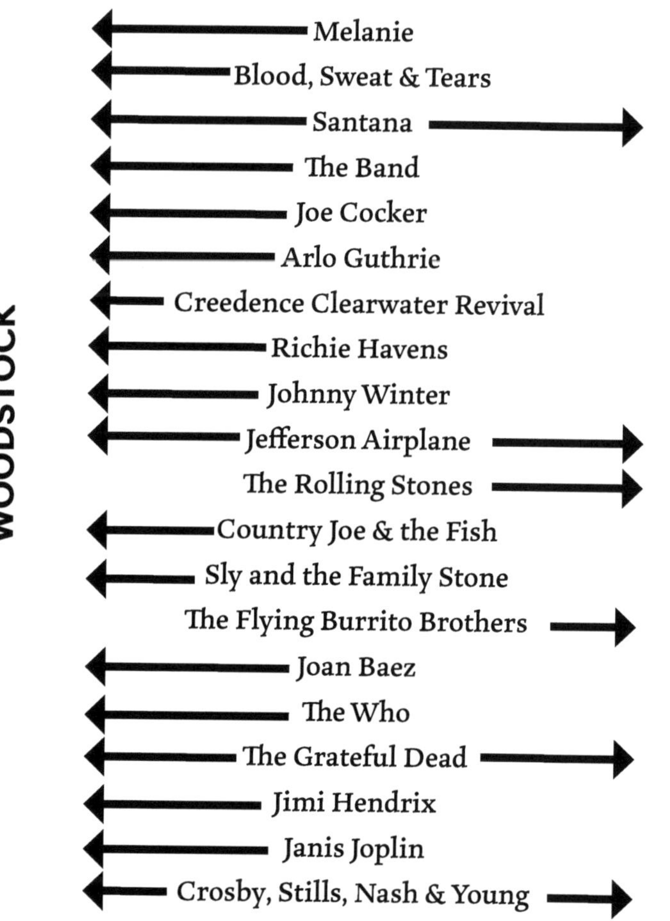
WOODSTOCK
ALTAMONT
Melanie
Blood, Sweat & Tears
Santana
The Band
Joe Cocker
Arlo Guthrie
Creedence Clearwater Revival
Richie Havens
Johnny Winter
Jefferson Airplane
The Rolling Stones
Country Joe & the Fish
Sly and the Family Stone
The Flying Burrito Brothers
Joan Baez
The Who
The Grateful Dead
Jimi Hendrix
Janis Joplin
Crosby, Stills, Nash & Young

1. **What was the name of Aimee Mann's band in the 1980s?**
   a. Pretty in Pink
   b. Timbuk3
   c. A-ha
   d. 'Til Tuesday

2. **Hot Tuna started as a side-project of members of which San Francisco band?**
   a. Jefferson Airplane
   b. The Grateful Dead
   c. The Greg Kihn Band
   d. The Tubes

3. **Who of the following was never officially part of the Wailers?**
   a. Bob Marley
   b. Lee "Scratch" Perry
   c. Peter Tosh
   d. Bunny Wailer

4. **What CSNY song has been called the greatest protest record and was banned from many radio stations when it came out in 1970?**

ANSWERS

1. **'Til Tuesday**

   She wrote their 1985 MTV staple, "Voices Carry."

   Recommended Album(s): *Voices Carry*

2. **Jefferson Airplane**

   Airplane guitarist Jorma Kaukonen and bassist Jack Casady formed the band while waiting for Grace Slick to recover from throat surgery. When she got better, they ended up opening for their main band and have been playing together since 1969.

   Recommended Album(s): *Burgers*

3. **Lee "Scratch" Perry**

   Some of their early songs were recorded with him and his house band, the Upsetters, and he produced them, but was never in the band, per se.

   Recommended Album(s): *Best of the Wailers*

4. **"Ohio"**

   It was released as a single (with Stephen Stills' "Find the Cost of Freedom" on the b-side) and didn't make it on an album until the compilation, *So Far,* in 1974.

   Recommended Album(s): You should find a 45 of it.

1. **According to PJ Harvey, " _______was a sacred name in our household," leading her to cover whose "Highway 61 Revisited" on Rid of Me?**

   a. Bob Dylan
   b. Neil Young
   c. Muddy Waters
   d. Johnny Cash

2. **What Rebecca Black tune from 2011 (with over 150 million views on YouTube) asked the pressing question, which seat can I take?**

   a. Tuesday
   b. The Dark and Disturbing World in Which We Live
   c. Friday
   d. The Importance of Being Earnest

3. **Which Chuck Berry tune did Dion (1964), Buck Owens (1969), Johnny Winter (1970), and Peter Tosh (1983) all have hit singles with?**

   a. Johnny B. Goode
   b. Rock and Roll Music
   c. Maybelline
   d. Sweet Little Sixteen

4. **Who produced a record 30 #1 singles, his biggest being "Hey Jude"?**

ANSWERS

1. **Bob Dylan**

   Harvey both upped the blues quotient of Dylan's original and punkified it.

   Recommended Album(s): *Rid of Me*

2. **"Friday"**

   Hey, she was a kid making a pop song. What the hell were you doing when you were 13?

   Recommended Album(s): Compare the original to the 2021 remix with Big Freedia.

3. **"Johnny B. Goode"**

   The Beatles, The Sex Pistols, The Grateful Dead, and Marty McFly, of course, all covered the Berry tune as well.

   Recommended Album(s): Find a good compilation of his Chess recordings.

4. **George Martin**

   Non-Beatles artists include America, Robin Gibb, and Kenny Rogers.

   Recommended Album(s): Compare *Let it Be* and *Let It Be...Naked* and you decide.

1. **When did Destiny's Child's debut come out?**
   a. 1994
   b. 1996
   c. 1998
   d. 2000

2. **What was the name of the concert film of Beyoncé's 2018 Coachella shows?**
   a. *Lemonade*
   b. *Lemon Stand*
   c. *Homecoming*
   d. *Far From Home*

3. **Who appears in Destiny's Child's Bootylicious video (and whose "Edge of Seventeen" was sampled in the song)?**
   a. Mariah Carey
   b. Aretha Franklin
   c. Belinda Carlisle
   d. Stevie Nicks

4. **In what movie did Beyoncé play FBI agent, Foxxy Cleopatra?**

ANSWERS

1. **1998**

   It featured the singles, "No, No, No" and "With Me," peaking at #67 overall. A taste of things to come.

   Recommended Album(s): *Destiny's Child*

2. ***Homecoming***

   Considered one of the best concert films ever, it was nominated for six Emmys and won the Grammy for Best Music Film.

   Recommended Album(s): *HΘMΣCΘMING: THE LIVE ALBUM*

3. **Stevie Nicks**

   They met while both doing promotion at NBC in NYC, after Beyoncé had already sampled the guitar riff from Nicks' "Edge of Seventeen." And three years later *bootylicious* entered the dictionary.

   Recommended Album(s): *Survivor*

4. ***Austin Powers in Goldmember***

   She plays a parody (homage?) to blaxploitation 1970s heroines. The soundtrack also features her first solo single, "Work It Out."

   Recommended Album(s): *Austin Powers in Goldmember*

1. **The first six albums to hold the title of best selling album of all the time were all musicals (and one comedy) album. Who was the first musical artist (but not, you know, musical) to hold the title?**
    a. Elvis Presley
    b. The Beatles
    c. Carole King
    d. Madonna

2. **Who is the highest-grossing artist from touring as a solo artist?**
    a. Madonna
    b. Justin Timberlake
    c. Beyoncé
    d. Kanye West

3. **Which Fleetwood Mac song featured 100 members of the USC marching band?**
    a. Stand Back
    b. Second Hand News
    c. Don't Stop
    d. Tusk

4. **What 1977 album has the most sales all time by a solo artist not named Michael Jackson?**

ANSWERS

1. **Carole King**

   Tapestry came out in 1971 and passed *The Sound of Music* in 1973, which then took back the crown in 1975, before *Tapestry* came back in 1976.

   Recommended Album(s): *Home*

2. **Madonna**

   $1.5 *billion*. But that's gross proceeds. Those conical bras don't come cheap.

   Recommended Album(s): *The Immaculate Collection*

3. **"Tusk"**

   You see, in the 1970s, this sort of thing made sense and if Mick Fleetwood wanted the USC marching band to come to Dodger Stadium and play, then damn right they will.

   Recommended Album(s): *Tusk*

4. ***Bat Out of Hell* by Meatloaf**

   It led to *Bat Out of Hell II: Back into Hell* and *Bat Out of Hell III: The Monster Is Loose. The Bodyguard Soundtrack* has more singers than just Whitney Houston, so it doesn't count.

   Recommended Album(s): *Bat Out of Hell*

SCRAMBLED ALBUMS

Can you decode the classic albums below?

Jilted Piglet Gall

It would very ironic if this had been the original title of this 1995 album. Although the dictionary folks might argue with your definition of irony, don't you think?

Metro Fairytales

This album is one of the building blocks of sludge metal and this title could have fit, unless it makes it sound too much like a young adult magic realism romance.

Organ Gambit

The actual title of this 1971 psychedelic funk masterpiece also has biological underpinnings, if perhaps a tad more unsettling.

Renegade Meat

If you didn't know what happened last Friday night, would you blame renegade meat?

SCRAMBLED ALBUMS

Jilted Piglet Gall
Jagged Little Pill

Alanis Morissette: 1995
"You Oughta Know," "Hand in My Pocket," "Ironic," "You Learn," and more. The gall was there and it was awesome.

Metro Fairytales
Master of Reality

Black Sabbath: 1971
Guitarist Tony Iommi, having sensitive fingers due to losing their tips in a factory accident, downtuned his strings and the bassist followed suit. But then Ozzy sang even higher.

Organ Gambit
Maggot Brain

Funkadelic: 1971
The title track took one take, when a tripping George Clinton told the guitarist to play like he was told his mother just died.

Renegade Meat
Teenage Dream

Katy Perry: 2010
She reportedly gave her producer, Dr. Luke, a mixtape of ABBA and the Cardigans and said we're going for that sound.

1. **Which band sued toy maker GoldieBlox for their unlicensed (or fair-use parody?) version of "Girls"?**
    a. The Beatles
    b. The Prodigy
    c. Oasis
    d. Beastie Boys

2. **In 1985 who made the heartland care about the summer of '69?**
    a. John Cougar
    b. John Cougar Mellencamp
    c. Bryan Adams
    d. Bruce Springsteen

3. **What "Godfather of Rhythm and Blues," son of Greek immigrants, had his biggest hit with "Willie and the Hand Jive"?**
    a. Johnny Otis
    b. Les Paul
    c. Johnny Ace
    d. Hank Ballard

4. **Who holds the record for most US top 40 hits by an American band, with 36?**

ANSWERS

1. **Beastie Boys**

   Although they thought GoldieBlox's goal of encouraging STEM skills in young girls was admirable, they felt constrained by Adam Yauch's will which said their music should never be used in ads. The two sides settled, with GoldieBlox donating $1 million to support STEM education for girls.

   Recommended Album(s): *License to Ill*

2. **Bryan Adams**

   Since Adams was only ten in 1969, it's *possible* the title refers to something else, but we can't, for the life of us, figure out what.

   Recommended Album(s): You could buy *Cuts Like a Knife*, but you don't have to....But now I'm looking stuff up and he's done a lot of charity work. And in 2019 he literally paddled his boat in front of a whale to intervene and block a whaling ship, so yeah, go buy some Bryan Adams. He has officially passed Ryan Adams in the cred department.

3. **Johnny Otis**

   His son, Shuggie, joined his band at 15 and later cut some great albums on his own and with Al Kooper.

   Recommended Album(s): *Original Show*

4. **The Beach Boys**

   From "Surfin'" in 1961 to the #1 "Kokomo" in 1988.

   Recommended Album(s): *Pet Sounds* isn't very hit-single-y, so I'm going with the *Endless Summer* compilation.

1. **Who was the only member of the Byrds present in every lineup?**
   a. Gram Parsons
   b. Roger McGuinn
   c. David Crosby
   d. Gene Clark

2. **Who organized The Rainbow Concert, to spur Eric Clapton (suffering from heroin addiction and other issues) to get his act back together?**
   a. Pete Townshend
   b. Steve Winwood
   c. Ronnie Wood
   d. Jim Capaldi

3. **Which hit Pat Benatar song was from her live album, *Live from Earth*, although it was a studio recording?**
   a. We Belong
   b. Love Is a Battlefield
   c. Looking for a Stranger
   d. Hit Me with Your Best Shot

4. **Who made her first recorded appearance as Little Ann on the single "Boxtop" in 1958, produced by her eventual husband (and then ex-husband)?**

ANSWERS

1. **Roger McGuinn**

   He was also the only Byrd the label trusted to actually play instruments on their first single, the #1 "Mr. Tambourine Man"; instead, they brought in LA session musicians from the Wrecking Crew, including Leon Russell.

   Recommended Album(s): *Mr. Tambourine Man, Sweetheart of the Rodeo*

2. **Pete Townshend**

   All of those artists supported Clapton at the show on January 13th, 1973 at the Rainbow Theater in London.

   Recommended Album(s): *Eric Clapton's Rainbow Concert*

3. **"Love is a Battlefield"**

   Pat Benatar called up songwriting friend Mike Chapman and asked for a hit song. He said, well, I'm sitting with Holly Knight right now, we'll write it right now. The writers first thought she did it too up-tempo and the record company asked what the hell was up with the drum loop, but it worked out for her.

   Recommended Album(s): *Live from Earth*

4. **Tina Turner**

   Her given name was Anna Mae Bullock (or possibly not). Ike Turner called her Tina (rhyming with Sheena, Queen of the Jungle) Turner, and then trademarked that name, so he could replace her with another "Tina Turner" when she left. There's a lot to untangle there. I'm on her side, in case you're wondering.

   Recommended Album(s): *Chess Box*

REVOLVING MEMBERS

Band members come and go, sometimes tragically, sometimes amicably, sometimes not-so-amicably. Sometimes an artist calls their manager and says to tell the band they're leaving. Sometimes a simple fax is enough to tell the gang you're leaving.

Syd Barret's drug use and general mental condition meant that he was in no shape to lead Pink Floyd. But they were able to soldier on. But when Jim Morrison died, maybe it wasn't worth it to try to keep the Doors going.

A band like the Allman Brothers might have enough talent to keep ramblin' on, even after a founding brother and guitar virtuoso dies. And sometimes the band reaches new heights with new blood.

On the next two pages match the original member with the band he left and then who replaced him.

ORIGINAL MEMBER	BAND
Chuck Mosley	Stone Temple Pilots
Freddie Mercury	Yes
Brian Jones	Queen
Bon Scott	AC/DC
Steve Marriott	Van Halen
David Lee Roth	Small Faces
Scott Weiland	Black Sabbath
Jon Anderson	Black Flag
Ozzy Osbourne	Journey
Gregg Rolle	Faith No More
Keith Morris	The Rolling Stones

BAND	REPLACEMENT MEMBER
Stone Temple Pilots	Brian Johnson
Yes	Sammy Hagar
Queen	Chester Bennington
AC/DC	Gary Cherone
Van Halen	Trevor Horn
Small Faces	Ronnie James Dio
Black Sabbath	Mike Patton
Black Flag	Mick Taylor
Journey	Ian Gillan
Faith No More	Henry Rollins
The Rolling Stones	Paul Rodgers
	Ron Wood
	Rod Stewart
	Steve Perry

ORIGINAL MEMBER	BAND

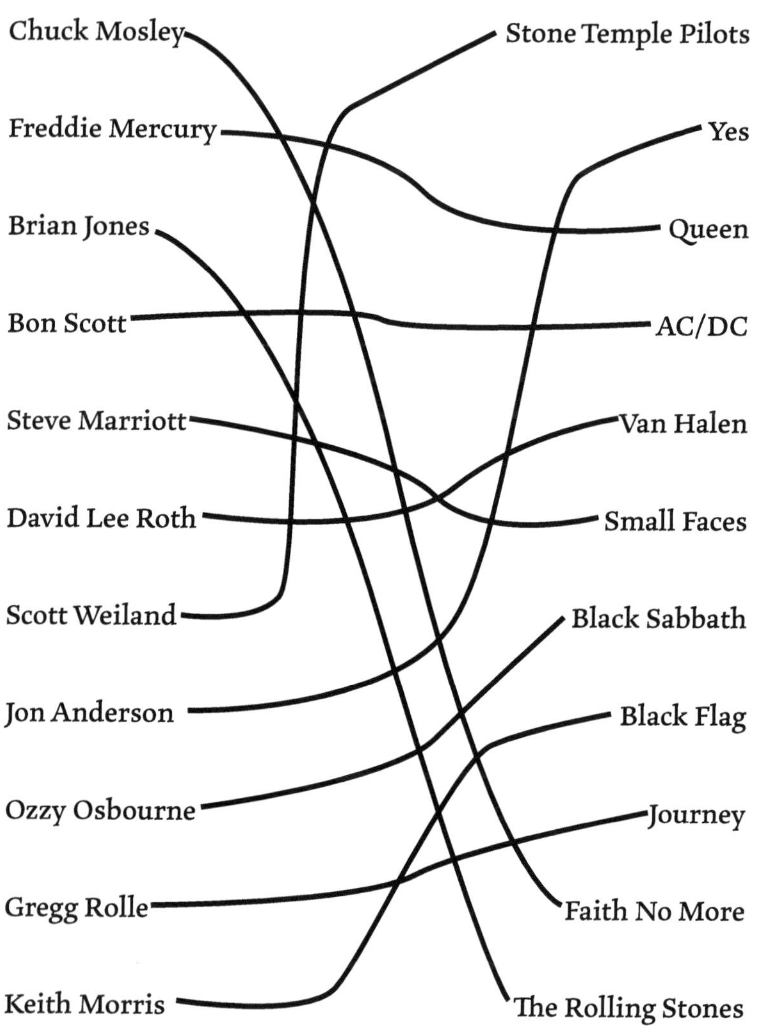
Chuck Mosley
Freddie Mercury
Brian Jones
Bon Scott
Steve Marriott
David Lee Roth
Scott Weiland
Jon Anderson
Ozzy Osbourne
Gregg Rolle
Keith Morris
Stone Temple Pilots
Yes
Queen
AC/DC
Van Halen
Small Faces
Black Sabbath
Black Flag
Journey
Faith No More
The Rolling Stones

BAND **REPLACEMENT MEMBER**

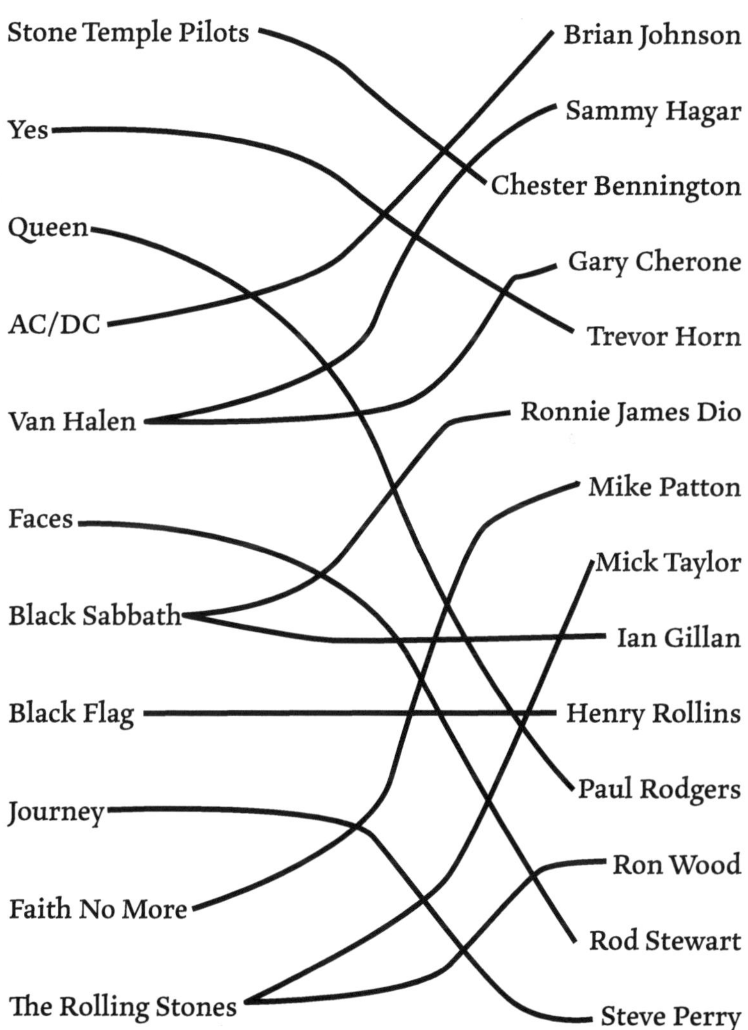

Stone Temple Pilots
Yes
Queen
AC/DC
Van Halen
Faces
Black Sabbath
Black Flag
Journey
Faith No More
The Rolling Stones
Brian Johnson
Sammy Hagar
Chester Bennington
Gary Cherone
Trevor Horn
Ronnie James Dio
Mike Patton
Mick Taylor
Ian Gillan
Henry Rollins
Paul Rodgers
Ron Wood
Rod Stewart
Steve Perry

REVOLVING MEMBERS

Stone Temple Pilots: After tensions in the band, they fired Scott Weiland and replaced him with Linkin Park's Chester Bennington. Early: *Purple* Later: *High Rise* ep

Yes: When Rick Wakeman and Jon Anderson left Yes, their manager brought in the Buggles' Geoff Downes and Trevor Horn, with some members forming Asia. Early: *Close to the Edge* Late: *Drama*

Queen: First up, Queen is a great band even without Freddie Mercury. Secondly, Free's/Bad Company's Paul Rodgers wasn't replacing Freddie, he was just letting people enjoy more Queen. Ditto with Adam Lambert. Early: *A Night at the Opera*

AC/DC: Singer Bon Scott tragically died of acute alcohol poisoning. The band debated breaking up, but decided to bring in Brian Johnson and dedicate an album to Scott. It sold 50 million copies. Early: *Powerage* Late: *Back in Black*

Van Halen: Less tragically, David Lee Roth wanted to go solo. They brought in Sammy Hagar and had more hits, then he left & they brought in Gary Cherone from Extreme and did not have more hits. Then Hagar came back and so did Roth. Early: *1984* Late: *5150*

Faces: Small Faces were a top mod group, until Steve Marriott left to form Humble Pie. In came Rod Stewart, who made the renamed Faces one of the best live bands of all time. Early: *Ogden's Nut Gone Flake* Late: *A Nod's As Good As a Wink... to a Blind Horse*

Black Sabbath: News Alert: Ozzy was a handful. So, he got fired in 1979. Early: *Paranoid* Late: *Heaven and Hell*

Black Flag: Fan Rollins climbed on stage and never left. Early: *Nervous Breakdown* ep Late: *My War*

Journey: Steve Perry joined the band late and left early. Early: *Journey* Late: *Escape*

Faith No More: Mosley sang on the first two albums but was too erratic to keep. Early: *Introduce Yourself* Late: *Angel Dust*

The Rolling Stones: Jone's drug problems were too much for the band (!) and they let him go (he died a month later); they then got Mick Taylor from John Mayall's Bluesbreakers and later got Faces' Ron Wood. Early: *Beggars Banquet* Late: *Exile on Main Street*

1. **Who had the best-selling album of the 2000s?**
    a. Eminem
    b. Usher
    c. Beyonce
    d. Jack White

2. **Which of the following were NOT part of Bob Dylan's 1975 Rolling Thunder Revue Tour?**
    a. Robbie Robertson
    b. Joan Baez
    c. Joni Mitchell
    d. Roger McGuinn
    e. Mick Ronson

3. **Whose debut single, "drivers license," hit #1 for eight weeks, the record for a debut?**
    a. Olivia Rodrigo
    b. James Brown
    c. Justin Bieber
    d. Kiki Dee

4. **In 1997, this re-recorded song spent 14 weeks at #1, reflecting consumers' love for the people's princess.**

ANSWERS

1. **Eminem**

   The Marshall Mathers LP sold over 21 million copies, back when people bought albums.

   Recommended Album(s): *The Marshall Mathers LP*

2. **Robbie Robertson**

   Allen Ginsberg showed up for a bunch of dates, too. Basically, they would ignore the big cities and just surprise local towns.

   Recommended Album(s): Watch the Martin Scorsese film, *Rolling Thunder Revue: A Bob Dylan Story*, even the parts he made up.

3. **Olivia Rodrigo**

   She's younger than you, a better songwriter than you, and is a bigger Disney star than you. (If you're younger than her, thank you very much for buying this book.)

   Recommended Album(s): *Sour*

4. **"Candle in the Wind 1997" by Elton John**

   The only time Elton John sang this version publicly was at Diana's funeral.

   Recommended Album(s): *Goodbye Yellow Brick Road*

1. **What French electronic duo disbanded in 2021 after 27 years, although they could have just found two humanoids who were the right heights and who would know the difference?**
    a. Devo
    b. Stardust
    c. Daft Punk
    d. Parcels

2. **Who wanted half the publishing rights from Dolly Parton in order to cover her song, "I Will Always Love You"?**
    a. Elvis Presley
    b. Whitney Houston
    c. Barbra Streisand
    d. Madonna

3. **What song has been dueted by Alicia Keys & Bono, Peter Gabriel & Kate Bush, and Willie Nelson & Sinead O'Connor?**
    a. Fairytale of New York
    b. American Tune
    c. At Last
    d. Don't Give Up

4. **What 1958 Link Wray song is the only instrumental banned by US radio stations?**

ANSWERS

1. **Daft Punk**

   Memorable for their helmeted outfits, Daft Punk's 2013 album *Random Access Memories* went to #1 in the US and dozens of other countries.

   Recommended Album(s): *Random Access Memories*

2. **Elvis Presley**

   Dolly said no. She had to wait almost 20 years, but I think Whitney Houston's version made up for it.

   Recommended Album(s): Parton's *Jolene*

3. **"Don't Give Up"**

   The original was done for Gabriel's *So* in 1986 (although he had hoped to get Dolly Parton to do it with him). The Alicia Keys & Bono version was a 2005 benefit for the Keep a Child Alive charity, to help AIDS/HIV-affected communities in Africa and India.

   Recommended Album(s): *So,* Nelson's *Across the Borderline*

4. **"Rumble"**

   Bob Dylan called it the best instrumental ever and Iggy Pop said it led him to his career in music.

   Recommended Album(s): Good luck finding a Link Wray compilation that doesn't have at least one version of the song.

Thanks to everyone for their help with this book, but especially to Allegra Matthews for cover and layout design and Megan Mullin for editorial assistance.

Made in the USA
Columbia, SC
11 December 2023

28257134R00100